The educational **poetry** competition combining literacy and history

Travel In Rhyme

London & Hertfordshire

First published in Great Britain in 2012 by:

 Young**Writers**

Remus House
Coltsfoot Drive
Peterborough
PE2 9BF
Telephone: 01733 890066
Website: www.youngwriters.co.uk

Foreword

Young Writers was established in 1991, dedicated to encouraging reading and creative writing by young people. Our nationwide writing initiatives are designed to inspire ideas and the incentive to write, and in turn develop literacy skills and confidence, whilst participating in a fun, imaginative activity. The final reward is the opportunity for the budding young writer to see their work in print.

Our latest competition, *Travel Back In Rhyme*, focuses on using historical periods, events or people to inspire poetry. The resulting collection is an illuminating glimpse into the past through the eyes of our young generation. There is verse inspired by everything from dinosaurs and cavemen, to the ancient civilisations of Greece and Egypt, to the World Wars and even space travel. The talented young poets have created verse that is gory, funny, dramatic, tragic: a reflection of human history up to the present day.

Using a mix of imagination, expression and historical inspiration, this anthology is an impressive snapshot of the inventive, original and skilful writing of young people today. With the extra bonus of fun fact pages about some of history's best bits, this collection is a journey back in time that will delight readers for years to come.

Contents

Purwell Primary School, Hitchin

St Joseph's Catholic Primary School, Bishop's Stortford

St Margaret Clitherow RC Primary School, Stevenage

Tower Primary School, Ware

West Green Primary School, London

William Patten Primary School, Stoke Newington

The Poetry

Space Landing

How exciting, newsflash, newsflash!
This is all happening in a dash!
Man has landed on the moon,
President Kennedy hoped it would be soon!

An American astronaut, Neil Armstrong,
Had trained for so long!
His friend Buzz Aldrin was also present,
Amazed that the moon was so pleasant!

1960 will be remembered in time,
Making history bells chime!
The Apollo 11 had landed on the moon,
The astronauts were going to step on it real soon!

The cameras were ready to go,
The men would be moving slow,
The force of gravity in space,
Gave a fun end to this race!

The lunar module Eagle, stood secure on the ground,
Neil and Buzz in their suits floating around,
Inside, gravity there was none,
So the astronauts had some fun!

There were craters and mountains for all to see,
And surprise, surprise, the moon is not made of cheese!
Neil Armstrong's historic words, 'That's one small step for man,
One giant leap for mankind'
Will forever be in our minds!

Neil and Buzz had a good look around,
Soon they would be homeward bound!
They took some photos and put up an American flag,
I wonder if they would have suffered any jet lag?

Emily King (9)
Ashtree Primary School, Stevenage

1

First Step On The Moon

I sat on the sofa
I turned on the telly
The brave Neil Armstrong
Was absolutely ready

So what was he ready for?
I assume you'll ask
He was landing on the moon
That's an amazing task

The rocket blasted off
It was a breathtaking view
What could happen?
Nobody knew

Whoosh, whoosh, whooosh
That's all I could hear
I said, 'Come on, Neil Armstrong
Take away that fear.'

He got out of the spaceship
I was very scared
Nobody disturbed the moment
Nobody even dared

He stepped on the moon
With a big, massive thump
I was so excited
That it made me jump

Everyone cheered
They were all so surprised
The brave Neil Armstrong
Deserved a fabulous prize

Hooray, hooray
Everyone cheered
But was there a problem?
I really feared

After two whole hours
My fears went away
Neil Armstrong
Had an important say:

*'One small step for man
One giant step for mankind!'*

Ilína Georgíeva (9)
Ashtree Primary School, Stevenage

Neil Armstrong Lands On The Moon

He has always dreamed of stepping on the moon,
Even when he was a little toddler,
And his dream is finally coming true.
Neil cannot believe that he is the first man stepping on the moon.

It feels strange, like a rock-hard ice cube,
He steps a step, which turns into a giant leap,
The moon is like a trampoline,
As bouncy as a rubber ball,
From there he sees a blue and green marble,
Oh, how small Earth is from where he is.

Silence is all around him,
Not a whisper or a whimper,
It is the quietest place ever visited.
The stars are beautiful from where he is,
The sun is even smaller than ever seen,
There are no trees, no bushes, no plants,
All he can see is the twinkling stars, the shining sun and our home, Earth.

The clouds seem so far away,
So near to the Earth,
It seems as if they're Sellotaped to Earth,
Oh, it's such a beautiful sight from the plain moon,
But he can't stay on the moon all day, he has to go home.

He takes one last leap and waves goodbye to the fascinating moon,
He goes back to his spaceship filled with joy
And whispers to himself, *I'll be back one day, I'll be back*
And sets off with a blast away from the moon.

Maëlle Cremmer
Ashtree Primary School, Stevenage

Theseus And The Minotaur

As Theseus set sail,
For the place the Minotaur laid,
The winds became stronger,
But he wasn't getting paid.

He put up the flags
And he got whisked away,
But they looked like rags
And failed by the end of the day.

He finally reached the maze,
He wasn't frightened at all.
Theseus looked at it with a rather strong gaze,
Thor started to roar and hail started to fall.

The Minotaur screeched,
As he got very hungry.
Theseus started to charge,
He became really angry.

A hoplite ran
To spread the news,
Theseus went with him
And the celebrations began.

So Theseus' glory
Came to an end,
The world knew his story
And it drove him round the bend!

Cheyenne-Lia Davies (10)
Ashtree Primary School, Stevenage

The Minotaur

I am the mighty Minotaur,
I am strong and tough,
And these are the things that make me
So fierce.
My fists are like lightning bolts
Striking the ground,
My roar of anger and frustration
Is like Hell rising.
My heart is the Devil's pitchfork,
Ready to stab any human being,
My teeth are like daggers
Which surround my mouth in pain.
My breath smells of human flesh,
Rotting in my masculine stomach,
My legs are as quick as lightning
In the darkness of my labyrinth.
My beaming eyes can see in the dark
And cause my prey to paralyse in fear.
I can never be defeated,
I am the Minotaur,
So beware!

Samuel Wiggins (10)
Ashtree Primary School, Stevenage

Moon Landing

M agnificent moon
O xygen masks on
O pportunities are big
N othing like a cool moon

L anding here is awesome
A ll around me is space
N eon colours
D usty ground
I nfinite space and never-ending time
N othing here so I begin
G ently bouncing up and down.

Holly Warren (9)
Ashtree Primary School, Stevenage

The Travel Diary Of Neil Armstrong

I'm sitting here in my rocket
Holding my lucky charm in my pocket
I feel nervous from my toes
Going up to my nose
5, 4, 3, 2, 1!
The blast is hotter than the sun
We lift off into space
We look around, it is a great place
The Earth looks like a giant sphere
It is crazy being up here
We have to find a safe landing spot
I cry, 'You don't find them a lot!'
The surface of the moon is rough and bumpy
It is also very lumpy
'One small step for men, one giant leap for mankind'
Rocks and sand is all I find
I am feeling proud being first on the moon
We'll be back on Earth very soon
I can't wait to see my family
I will live ever so happily.

Evan Egan
Ashtree Primary School, Stevenage

Moon Landing Of 1969

Moon landing on 20th July 1969,
Neil Armstrong, first person to land on the moon,
That's one small step for man,
One giant leap for mankind.
The crew were trying to land Apollo 11,
Neil looked out of the window,
He found boulders and rocks,
Took control panel in his hands,
Landed when fuel nearly ran out.
The astronauts were extremely happy,
When they first touched the moon's surface,
A goal achieved that people thought was impossible.

Khush Haria (9)
Ashtree Primary School, Stevenage

6

Lunar Landing

L unar landing Apollo 11 was the space flight which landed the first humans on the moon on July 20th, 1969.

U SS Hornet was the recovery ship that picked up the astronauts from the Pacific Ocean.

N eil Armstrong was the first man to walk on the moon, 'That's one small step for man, one giant leap for mankind'.

A stronauts, Neil Armstrong, Edwin 'Buzz' Aldrin and Michael Collins were Apollo 11's crew.

R e-entering the Earth's atmosphere caused a huge fireball.

L unar rocks were brought back to Earth from the moon.

A n American flag was left on the moon's surface.

N ASSA sent the astronauts with a number of scientific experiments to set up.

D angerous mission to the moon was successful!

I t was viewed on television by 500 million people.

N ixon - while on the moon the astronauts received a call from President Richard Nixon.

G ravity was reduced on the moon. This meant that the astronauts could jump very high compared to Earth.

Ben Conquest (9)
Ashtree Primary School, Stevenage

They Landed On The Moon

In 1969 astronauts landed on the moon
They said it could not be done!
The rocket they used was called Apollo 11
They said it could not get there!
It was rumoured the landing was fake, but it was true,
It cost millions of dollars to fund the landing,
Some said was it worth it?
The rocket was fired from Cape Canaveral
They said it would explode!
Millions watched the landing on telly
Mostly in black and white.
The moon was found lifeless
Many said, oh what a shame!

Charlotte Payne (9)
Ashtree Primary School, Stevenage

7

I Am Theseus

Leaving Ariadne was a mistake, but I had to,
I will not forget her.
My heart is thumping from the monster,
But he lies still now.
His body is broken, his heart has stopped,
I have taken his soul.

I have killed the terrifying Minotaur,
I am the town hero,
It all feels like a dream,
I have succeeded.

I am Theseus and I will have a story,
I will be famous and everyone will know me,
The city will sit in peace,
My dad will be proud.

I've got a perfect life and it could not change,
I have listened to my father,
I have achieved my purpose,
My task is done.

Nyarli Calderon (11)
Ashtree Primary School, Stevenage

Travel Back In Rhyme

I can see pitch-black around me in the deadly mist.
It's messing with my mind as I tiptoe towards the nightmares.
The deadly mist is my cold breath as I panic and I cannot escape it.
It's making me feel petrified, scared
And it fills me up with temper, like the angry Devil's pitchfork
With its sharp, pointy ends as it emerges against me,
It might pierce my heart and my soul screams with anxious fears,
Beginning to threaten my body as it shivers down my spiky spine
As it keeps tempting me to go further on with the ball of string
And my dangerous tools to fight the terrible monster.
I hear my footsteps tapping on the rough ground
And I suddenly stop in silence after I had defeated the outrageous Minotaur
As he falls with a thud in the sticky mud.

Caitlin Gover (10)
Ashtree Primary School, Stevenage

Poseidon, God Of The Seas

I am Poseidon
I command the seas
I protect the sea creatures
My waves will take down your ships in fury
And make them sink down to the depths of the sea
Never to be seen again.

I am Poseidon
I hold my trident that's gold like the sun
With devastating power
I'll use the power of the moon
To force tides in upon you.

I am Poseidon
If you ignore me or upset me
I will strike the Earth with my trident
And shake the Earth in horror
Until you've learnt your lesson.

I am Poseidon, do not mess around with me.

Samuel Hardy (10)
Ashtree Primary School, Stevenage

The Minotaur

I let out a mighty roar,
I am the Minotaur,
I am as tough as can be,
So don't mess with me.
I am a terrifying beast,
And I will have you for my feast.
You will hear your bones crunch,
Like the crisps do in your lunch.
My grip is so tight,
But doesn't hurt as much as my bite.
My horns are really sharp,
And they have a dented mark.
I am the Minotaur
And I will never be destroyed!

Jessica Allum (11)
Ashtree Primary School, Stevenage

9

Travel Back In Rhyme

There once was a man called Bob,
He did not know where he was.
He was in a place where men were in dresses,
Then he realised they were gods and goddesses.
Then he turned to see people on a line ready to go,
The audience shouting and all screaming, 'No!'
He felt like he should do something to get them to stop,
But he was too late and the arrow was shot
And then they were off, ready to fight the huge beast,
The winner of this challenge would get a big feast.
It was then that he saw the creature for the first time,
Zeus and Hera holding goblets of wine.
They clapped and applauded for Theseus to win,
But seeing as he was losing, Zeus' patience was wearing thin.
With a sword and some string the beast was fought,
Mino's daughter, Ariadne, was no longer distraught.
The crowd went wild, the gods were pleased
And at last Theseus and Ariadne set sail across the Aegean Sea.

Nathan Jackson (10)
Ashtree Primary School, Stevenage

A Hoplite

Hoplites are brave like
A wild animal ready to eat,
Hoplites are strong like
A giant rugby player.
Hoplites are lions ready to
Pounce on their prey,
Hoplites are fearless like
Wasps stinging giants.
Hoplites are fierce like a
Bear grinding his teeth,
Hoplites are serious to
Do their jobs.
Beware of the Hoplites,
They are dangerous!

Nathan Stewart (10)
Ashtree Primary School, Stevenage

An Athenian Hoplite

A battle commenced in 490BC, Athenians against the Persians, we all fought for our lives.

H oplites from all over Athens joined together. We felt anxious, terrified and scared too.

O n the battlefield we fought and fought. There was blood everywhere and the stench of dead bodies filled our nostrils.

P ersian dead bodies were everywhere. They covered the whole of Marathon, you could hear them all screaming in pain.

L ots of lives were lost that day. It was very tragic for both the Persians and Athenians.

I t had ended, the Athenians had won. They had finally conquered the Persians once and for all.

T he Persians sailed off to Athens to do a surprise attack on us, but when they saw us coming, they decided to change their plans.

E cstatic Hoplites sailed back to Athens, the city was filled with happiness and joy. They had won the battle of Marathon, hooray!

Emilia Conquest (11)
Ashtree Primary School, Stevenage

Theseus In The Labyrinth

I was there in the labyrinth, waiting for an unexpected lash,
I couldn't see anything but darkness, I heard a big crash.
As I edged round corners with my dagger at my side,
I could hear other people. 'Help!' they cried.
My arms had goosebumps, my lip shivered,
I went round the corner, I quickly quivered,
He was there in front of me, I could feel his breath.
I looked into his eyes, I was scared to death,
I jabbed my dagger at his shin, then he stumbled.
He suddenly got up, he groaned and mumbled,
I leapt at him one more time.
I took him down in his prime.
I could see his blood, I knew he was dead,
For that, I now wear the king's crown on my head.

Ethan Antrobus (10)
Ashtree Primary School, Stevenage

First Man On The Moon

Don't be late,
The Eagle is coming,
Be on time,
Armstrong is humming!

Only 60 seconds left,
We're out of time,
Hurry up,
I can hear a chime!

They did it, they did it,
We all shout hooray,
No one got hurt,
They did it today.

Armstrong had done it,
But he wasn't blind,
He said, 'One step for man,
A giant leap for mankind'.

Michelle Bonuah (10)
Ashtree Primary School, Stevenage

Theseus And The Minotaur

I, Prince Theseus brave and strong,
Set off to kill the mighty Minotaur,
Half-man and half-bull!

I sweat to slay this terrible beast,
To stop him having a feast!

Walking through the dark, smelly maze,
I approached the fearless beast!
He was big and hairy and scary,
I was going to be his next feast.
I found some strength within me.
I twisted his horns from side to side,
His neck snapped, the beast had died.
I, Prince Theseus, have killed the mighty Minotaur!

Danny Wallis (10)
Ashtree Primary School, Stevenage

12

Zeus

I am Zeus, the most powerful god,
And all the other gods fear me.
I rule the heavens with an iron rod
And no one dares disobey me.

In the temples people come to pray,
At my statues they leave presents.
Praying for good fortune every day
And that I will make their lives pleasant.

There are many festivals because of me,
With singing and dancing too,
But all of them are great to see,
And some I want to do.

I want my people to do what I say
And to try and be kind and good.
As I am king they must obey
And behave as they always should.

Robert Gallagher (10)
Ashtree Primary School, Stevenage

Thor

I am Thor, I am thunder
I rule the sky
And if you do something bad
I snap at you with my lightning bolt!

I am anger, I am fire
Strong as oak
Fierce as a tornado
Raining down on you
Like a ton of stone.

The hammer that I carry
Protects all mankind
Beware enemies
For I am Thor!

Leon Taylor (11)
Ashtree Primary School, Stevenage

The Minotaur

As you enter the labyrinth . . .

I hear the door shut behind you
I listen for your footsteps.
I will track down where you are
When you get closer I hear your fearful breath

I see your shadow when you get closer
I look at the entrance all the time
I never leave my lookout space
You will regret being seen when I spot you

I am feeling very hungry now
Someone's coming and I'm ready to pounce
I shall trap them in my hands and eat them whole
Then I will feel very happy but still hungry

*Beware, I am the Minotaur
And I am coming for you.*

Jordan Cooper (10)
Ashtree Primary School, Stevenage

The Moon

Bright, high in the sky
Amongst stars, comets
And a Milky Way.

A rocket blasted through
Space and time
To a ghostly planet.

Landing bumpy on
The rocky surface.
A spaceman was amazed
Looking across a dull land.

One step forward and
Flag in hand
'One small step for man
And one giant leap for mankind.'

Jason Eyles (10)
Ashtree Primary School, Stevenage

Theseus

As I tiptoe through the labyrinth,
The midnight mist closes in on me,
My toes go tingly and fingers go numb.

As I cautiously turn now and then,
I suddenly catch a glimpse of the moonlight
Peeping through the trees.
My tummy churns and my heart pumps
Faster and faster, like a merry-go-round.

As I anxiously unravel my string,
My nose reacts from the stench of a pigsty
And my ears fade away from the dreadful roar
Of the Minotaur.

Any minute now, I'm edging towards
The worst nightmare ever.
My body doubting myself, although my heart determined.

Jodie Gunton (10)
Ashtree Primary School, Stevenage

The Moon Landing

We were sitting in our messy living room
With our black and white TV
It was the 20th July 1969
When Neil Armstrong and Buzz Aldrin
Were trying to land The Eagle on the moon
We were glued to our seats, terrified as
Their fuel was running low
And they could not find a flat surface
To land The Eagle.
Luckily, they found a safe place
To land without damaging the legs.
The people at NASA were holding their breath, turning blue
And so were we and then we heard the astronauts saying
'The Eagle has landed'
Then we started cheering and jumping up and down
My family will never forget that amazing day!

Alyssa Butterfield (9)
Ashtree Primary School, Stevenage

Theseus And The Minotaur

As Theseus walked into the labyrinth,
He could smell the foul smell of the Minotaur.
As he got closer it smelt worse
And all of a sudden, it got so bad he nearly fainted.

As Theseus walked on,
He could hear the Minotaur panting
Because he was very hungry.

As Theseus walked on,
He felt very nervous,
But determined at the same time.
But then he got really strong and brave.

Theseus saw nothing but pitch-black
And all of a sudden, he saw the Minotaur,
He was half-man and half-bull.

Emma Carter (10)
Ashtree Primary School, Stevenage

The Minotaur

The scary but lonely Minotaur
Sits in the maze upset.
It stands and cries
As it gets beaten.
I wince every time they whip it.
The Minotaur screams
As pain spreads.
Its tough, leathery skin
Gets weaker and weaker.
I think it should be let go
It just wants to make friends.
I feel more sorry
Each time I see it harmed.

Georgia Setterfield (10)
Ashtree Primary School, Stevenage

The Minotaur

I am the Minotaur
I live in the labyrinth and this is what I see
Dark, cold walls all around me
I search my maze looking for scraps of meat
I don't know where I am
However, I know I am in Crete
I have sharp horns which pierce through flesh
Crooked teeth and terrible breath
Don't go into the labyrinth
It is not a great place to be
If you are one of the seven boys or girls
You will be eaten by me.

Kian Hewstone (10)
Ashtree Primary School, Stevenage

Theseus

My name is Theseus, I live in Crete,
I can see a castle ruled by a king.
He has a Minotaur, within a labyrinth,
14 people sacrificed, 7 boys and 7 girls.
I swore I would defeat this beast,
Then fly my flag high, my quest complete,
I met a girl, who gave me a sword,
I slew the beast then went with her,
No flag I flew.
My dad found out and thought I was through,
He killed himself and I became king,
This is how my reign begins.

Michael Groom (10)
Ashtree Primary School, Stevenage

17

The Moon Landing

We were all gathered around our television,
Seemed like the whole streets were there,
Waiting for this transmission.

I was very anxious and nervous about the landing,
As we all held our breath, we were standing.
Then the Eagle landed with only 20 seconds of fuel left.
We all screamed and shouted, I am sure I went deaf!

As Armstrong appeared and started down the stairs,
The whole room just sat there and stared.
With the flag in hand, Armstrong proudly said,
'This is one small step for man.'

Harvey Joyce (9)
Ashtree Primary School, Stevenage

The Moon Landing

Three brave American astronauts went to the moon,
We all prayed they would come back safe and soon.

They landed safe and sound,
With craters all around.

Neil Armstrong was the first to walk on this faraway land,
The moon's surface looked just like grey sand.

All the thoughts that went through his mind when he said,
'One small step for man, one giant leap for mankind'.

They came back safe and sound,
To walk again on solid ground.

Chloe Reeves (10)
Ashtree Primary School, Stevenage

Moon Landing

M en launched into space 16th July 1969
O ut of the atmosphere they went
O ne small step for man, one giant leap for mankind
N eil Armstrong steps foot on the moon

L anded on 20th July 1969
A space buggy was driven on the moon
N eil and Buzz had fun on the moon.
D iscovering the moon was a lot of fun
I nto the sea the capsule splashed
N ow safely back home the astronauts are
G reatest journey of all time.

Keren Richardson (9)
Ashtree Primary School, Stevenage

The Underworld

I sit here on my throne of bones
Plotting revenge against my brothers,
Sending me here was awful,
Now it's more perfect than stupid souls could imagine!

I walk around passing by souls,
I hear the souls weeping and moaning.
I sail across the River Styx, waiting for the dead,
Looking at all the unfulfilled dreams.
I plan my schemes day and night,
I feel so alive because I know,
Someday my brothers will fall and I will rise!

Hannah Edgar (10)
Ashtree Primary School, Stevenage

Men On The Moon

Two men are going to the moon,
This is happening now at noon,
People are surprised it's happening so soon.

They are in space!
Wow, they are nearly at that place,
They're probably eating space food while others are wondering how it tastes.

They have landed on the moon!
One of them went out with a zoom.
Some people think they are staying there until June,
They could probably see a lagoon.

Danny Gondola (10)
Ashtree Primary School, Stevenage

The Minotaur

Here I sit waiting excitedly,
When the flesh comes in, it lights up my eyes.
I rummage through the skin and blood
Until I get to the bones,
I hear people screaming and then silence,
That makes me happy.
I see the dead bodies piling up,
That makes me hungry.
I feel delighted to have such a good feast.
I'm the Minotaur, don't mess with me!

David Cook (10)
Ashtree Primary School, Stevenage

The Minotaur

Beware, the Minotaur is coming, *roar!*
With his flesh-piercing horns
Which can rip through any human or beast's body.
As the Minotaur turns round rapidly with his glary, red eyes,
He then waits patiently for his next victim.
His big, hairy ears listen out
For the tiptoeing of the beast's next meal.
The labyrinth is all quiet,
In the centre of the dreadful maze, the Minotaur gets ready
For its last kill!

Jake Pickard (10)
Ashtree Primary School, Stevenage

The Minotaur's Fear

The Minotaur stands silent in the labyrinth,
Lonely and terrified.
The Minotaur can see the green, fresh bushes,
He can see the stony, crumbly concrete.
The Minotaur can hear the bushes waving in the wind
And footsteps that are getting louder every second.
The closer they get, the Minotaur gets more frightened.
The wind is blowing on the Minotaur's leather skin
And his fur gets colder as time goes by.
The Minotaur's waiting for the end.

Paris Jay Hubner (10)
Ashtree Primary School, Stevenage

Moon Landing

The first man on the moon was Neil Armstrong,
He was extremely brave and strong,
He took his first steps
And he almost wept,
But a very nervous person like him,
As you know made it a win.
But it was a big step for mankind,
He was the best you will ever find,
He held the flag with such joy,
Now he felt no longer a boy.

Sasha Mole
Ashtree Primary School, Stevenage

The Minotaur

I am a monster as dark as the midnight sky
I eat about 1,000 a year
I hear people screaming and if I hear footsteps
It's good because it means someone's coming
I see hardly anything, just black
If people come I can see a bit of their faces
I feel very bored because all I do is eat people all day
Have you guessed yet, if you haven't then I am . . .
The Minotaur!

Callum Myles (10)
Ashtree Primary School, Stevenage

Theseus

As I edge closer to the Minotaur in the dirty, dusty labyrinth
Tiptoeing my way around quietly, listening to the almighty roar
As I'm tiptoeing, I'm hearing the walls laughing at me
All I can see is pitch-black and nothing else
Still with all this going on, I feel confident with a hint of weakness
Taking my last few breaths and then *rrrroooaaarrr!*
The battle's on.

Robert Cook (10)
Ashtree Primary School, Stevenage

I Zeus

I am Zeus, greatest god of Mount Olympus
I spend my time on Mount Olympus
Watching people worship me
The top of Mount Olympus reaches heaven
Because it's so high, so I see everyone
I Zeus am happy to be king of the gods
Because I am in charge of the other gods and goddesses
I'm armed with thunder and lightning
Which is very frightening.

Alisha Trodden (10)
Ashtree Primary School, Stevenage

The Minotaur

I am your worst nightmare,
I will kill you because I am a flesh-eating monster.
My horns are needles digging into your skin,
My breath is as smelly as a skunk when it is protecting itself.
I can feel the lovely bones of my food,
I can hear the scared and agonising screams of my sacrifices.
I can see the walls of the maze nobody can get out of,
I feel alive and good.
I am the Minotaur and I am very hungry, so beware!

Neave Keeney (10)
Ashtree Primary School, Stevenage

The Minotaur

M an-eating beast
I nvincible beast
N asty when you make the encounter with the beast
O blivious to being killed
T errible smelling creature
A ppetite will never be lost
U nwanted by anyone
R *oar!* So scream before me because I am the Minotaur.

Nathan Chinn (10)
Ashtree Primary School, Stevenage

The Creepy Beast

The vast, titanic beast
Smells like pungent, rotten fruit
He's delighted when someone steps in his cave
He's fierce, horrible and miserable
He lives on blood
He lives in Mongola between Athens and Sparta
His pointy horns alarm you wherever you go
His bellowing roar can knock you out
'Boo! I'm the Minotaur!' *Roar!*

Emma Keane (10)
Ashtree Primary School, Stevenage

Minotaur

My hooves will crush you as you lie on the floor
You squirm as I devour you
I see you running for the escape
I track you down with my amazing sense of smell
I hear you screaming, screeching as I chase you
You feel petrified as you sneak around the maze
In the pitch-black darkness you hear me roar
Because I am the invincible Minotaur.

Joe Carroll (10)
Ashtree Primary School, Stevenage

Untitled

Apollo 11 is landing on the dusty moon,
There's no water,
No trees,
No people and no air,
Only white star dust.
Craters are bigger than a football pitch,
Scientists cheer and laugh,
Families happy and overjoyed.

Maks Czubala
Ashtree Primary School, Stevenage

The Minotaur

I am the Minotaur as fierce as can be,
Hungry like a lion, you'd better not mess with me.
I'm lurking around the maze, wandering about,
What's that I hear? Children no doubt.
Cold, damp and dark is the place where I live,
There is no one in the palace who I want to be with.
Theseus is the prince and thinks he is very strong,
But I am the Minotaur and I know he is very wrong!

Ashleigh Gardner (10)
Ashtree Primary School, Stevenage

The Moon Landing

The first man to go on the moon was Neil Armstrong,
He wore a spacesuit but couldn't stay for long.
He said, 'That's one step for mankind'
When he stood on the moon in 1969.
600 million people watching as he was jumping along the sky.
The ship was called Apollo 11 and it's short name was called Eagle.
Cape Kennedy, Florida is where it took off.
It went really fast and I know it was not the last.

Jake Reed
Ashtree Primary School, Stevenage

The Minotaur

I'm the thing you shiver about in your dreams,
The echo of my roar sinks into your head.
As you creep through the labyrinth, unaware of what's round the corner,
You will feel fear at every bend you turn.
You think, *shall I turn back or should I keep going?*
You can feel your blood chilling as you dart round every corner,
You can hear the petrified cries of your men.
I'm the Minotaur, so beware!

Euan Cairns (10)
Ashtree Primary School, Stevenage

The Moon Landing

On the glorious day in 1969
America says, 'The moon is mine'
The astronauts planted a flag
And collected moon rocks in a bag
When the men were on the moon
They knew they would be leaving soon
On the moon the men were here
But they had nothing to fear.

Owen Wilson
Ashtree Primary School, Stevenage

Untitled

Neil and Buzz on the moon
If you see them you will go blue.

When you take the first small step
Everyone is happy for the best.

'One small step for man, one giant step for mankind'
Were the first words said on the moon
That's when everyone turned blue.

Charlie Clarke
Ashtree Primary School, Stevenage

Homeland

As I look out across London, I can see the rubble
and remains of once-loved houses:
With floorboards sticking out like fingers from what looks like
the old Judge's house.
There was smoke and I could see flames over to the east,
yet everyone was acting as though it was a normal day.

I can smell the smoke from the raging fire that the firemen
were trying desperately to put out.
The faint smell of cigars wafting up from two men smoking below.
The smell of concrete, cement and old houses dominated the air.
Exhaust fumes from the many fire trucks
and aviation fuel from the Spitfires protecting us overhead.

I can only hope that the bombing raids will stop and that Germany surrenders;
that the burning infernos will stop
that the buildings will stop crumbling
I just hope this nightmare will end.

I can feel the crumbly rubble under my feet,
the dust and grit in the air.
I can feel water droplets in the air
and heat from the intense fire the hoses were dousing.
I can feel despair as owners of bombed houses try
to retrieve belongings from the piles of debris.

Maximilian Jacoby (11)
Bishop's Stortford College, Bishop's Stortford

The Destroying World War II

Set the scene in 1940 and you are looking out of
Buckingham Palace's finest window
I am the Queen.
What do I see?
Majestic banquets, ruby-red buses and once beautiful chimneys
Standing alone.
What do I smell?
Winston's coal-black cigar and fumes from the factories
Which are still standing tall.
What do I hope for?
Peace and happiness, no rainy days and our city's safety.
What do I dream of?
Blue, sunny skies and reunited families together at last.
What do I hear?
Pickaxes chopping away at the grubby rubble
That used to be fine buildings
And the traumatic screams of the children
Being taken away from their loving families.

Long live the Queen!

Isabel Farmer (10)
Bishop's Stortford College, Bishop's Stortford

The Doodlebug

The dingy, grey, winged doodlebug sailed through the polluted, dark sky,
Down on the ground you could hear the terrified children from the village cry.

People fled and scrambled into their gloomy, stuffy shelter,
The doodlebug raced down like a young child on a helter-skelter.

People were alert and knew what was going to hit them,
They could smell the fuel from the racing fire engine.

When the menacing doodlebug hit the deck, it gave an enormous *bang!*
And still the air raid siren rang.

Strong smoke came in clouds from the raging fire,
All that was left from the fire engine was a blazing tyre.

Emily Kerr (10)
Bishop's Stortford College, Bishop's Stortford

Soldier

A new dawn is breaking
Everyone is waking
The sun is warm on my only arm
I hope I will come to no further harm
I listen to the guns' dreadful boom
As I feel the return of doom.

I feel death all around me
Nothing but destruction can be seen
I feel like I'm in an endless dream
I let out a silent scream
I feel my soul evaporating away
And my body left behind to stay.

I smell the stench of dried blood on my uniform
And the ashes of fallen aircraft shot down in the dawn
I smell the sweat of tired soldiers sleeping
And can feel the fear of those still weeping.

As I drift far above the destruction below
My heart beats softly and begins to slow
My fear within begins to grow
I dream of the time when peace is around
And my family are all safe and sound.

Daniel Limb (10)
Bishop's Stortford College, Bishop's Stortford

Bomb

He hopes to hit a highly populated area.
His dream is to hit an important building or person.
He can already taste victory over the war.
The screams of people below him, pleases him dearly.

All his hopes are set on bombing Winston Churchill in his house.
Every day he dreams of bombing the king or queen.
The taste of smoke rising from the rubble.
The sound of death and misery puts him to rest.

His hope is to completely destroy London.
He only dreams about taking down Britain with one bomb.
He can already taste the destruction he will cause.
The sound of a bomb hitting the ground puts an end to all his worries.

He hopes to hit a factory making bullets and bombs.
The taste of winning a medal And the sound of everyone cheering his name.
His dream of conquering the world is bright.

Sam Moss (11)
Bishop's Stortford College, Bishop's Stortford

The Bomb!

I can hear a fizzing bomb ready to go off,
The rattling bomb trying to roll off the aircraft.
It's ready to burst and crack everywhere and get all the people watching.
I can see fire starting to burst out.
The coal-black colour getting lighter as it's getting hotter.
The string ready to fling off.
I can smell a minor smell.
The air smelling fairly evil.
The bomb building up the pong.
The bomb smelling like a horrid cauldron.
I can feel rumbling like in the jungle.
The bomb extremely solid.
The bomb as greasy as butter.
The bomb feeling all tingly on your hands.
The bomb went off, the flashing light blinding you.
Bang!

Sophie-Anne Alexander (10)
Bishop's Stortford College, Bishop's Stortford

Winston Churchill

The smell of his cigars as he's making a great speech
The smell of his leather jacket as he stands next to you
The enticing smell of the roast dinner he had for lunch
The smell of the freshly cut grass at his country estate

The dark bowler that is always perched on his head
The giganticness of his swinging stomach as he walks
The immaculate thousand pound suit covering his body
The intense stare as he addresses his waiting audience

The emotion as he makes his best speech
'Never in the field of human conflict was so much owed by so many to so few'
The emotion as he talks about his love of his country
'I have nothing to offer but blood, toil, tears and sweat'
His emotion as he talks about his place in history
'History will be kind to me as I intend to write it'
his emotion as he talks about his belief that he will survive the war.

Lewis Craig (10)
Bishop's Stortford College, Bishop's Stortford

The World Where Nothing Will Become

Grim faces cover the street,
Hunger eating through endless bodies,
Dead souls of children of which nothing will become,
Images lost through cruel, hard work,
We all suffer, but not like this,
Aching limbs swarming past decaying houses,
Many ponder their future,
Most dying from the curse of those times,
The waves of hope seeming miles away, untouchable,
The streets littered with filth.
Cries of sheer expressionless faces engulf the town.
People chase pavements but, where will they lead?
The dreaming continues.
The people all crazy for one reason, they want more, but
They are trapped in the world where nothing will become.

Caspar Schulze (10)
Canonbury Primary School, Islington

The Plague Of Poverty

What do you hope for?
What do you dream of?
I dream of equality though I know it will never come,
Especially for someone like me,
Who am I to anyone else?
Nothing,
And why should I be?

My brother's squirming, greasy hand, I clutch,
We shuffle along the gutter way,
Past towering rows of red brick houses we trudge,
Privileged homes we call them,
The repetitive cracking of a whip,
My eyes wander to the bright, elaborate carts clattering past,
Jealous they make me,
Like paper our fragile skin tears,
We scrape past the jutting walls,
Scents so pungent; stale sweat, rusting metal,
Washes over and bathes us like the water we never have,
I face my brother as a single raindrop trickles down his cheek,
But rather than comforting him as families do,
I collect the tear, grateful for God's gift,
Salt-filled tears,
The plague,
The plight of the poor,
That sweeps like a blanket over,
That starves and manufactures suffering.

But the raw pain of death that could come at any moment,
Yet alas, perhaps that would be better than this horrific life,
We pass a little girl coughing, starving, lying sprawled on the streets,
No time for her, you must fend for yourself,
But don't think badly of me,
Do you see anyone helping?
Uneven cobbles carpet the street,
Stained with mud and tragically, occasionally blood,
I look in the odd muddy puddle,
No more than a starving urchin I see.

Rosalind McDonald-Hill (10)
Canonbury Primary School, Islington

Poor Me!

Dark, gloomy alleyways,
Carriages lurching sideways,
Lights beaming down the streets,
I walk with bare feet,
Negotiating animals littering my home.

My heart pounding, my belly rumbling,
Making distraught murmuring,
Sadness, badness and frustration,
Hopeless, I feel weak,
But I have to work hard for my family!
Rats squealing,
Bellowing horns bleeping,
Children crying, poor parents sighing,
Rich owners, tradesmen laughing!

I touch dirty windows, my only mark on this world,
I work really hard,
I sweep muddy streets,
My family need to survive,
The water that I drink is filthy.

The misty air that I breathe,
Tastes of smoke from the factories!
Rubbish carelessly thrown away,
Blocking the drains . . .
Dead animals everywhere.

I hope to become rich one day,
To end this pitiful way of living
And have plenty of food on my plate.
I dream of being in charge of the state,
That's what I dream of, I hope it will be *true*.

Art Hoti (10)
Canonbury Primary School, Islington

The End

The street, my street, my home, covered in dirty snow,
Here and there, stinky brown splodges (of which you should not mention in
polite company),
I look down at my makeshift soup kitchen,
Its warmth, the only light in the dark.
Just one sip would fill my shrivelled, empty belly and cure my deathly starvation.
That is what I smell, death.
Of course the city stinks, of everything;
Unwashed clothes, the brown substance and pretty much anything unpleasant.
The poor, deranged man who lurks in the alleyway, is running around,
yelling in a strange language.
Once, he wrote a note telling me to stop dreaming,
But, I still dream – of food, a bed, of someone to care for me.
I hear a driver, cracking his whip,
Forcing his chestnut-brown horses to go faster.
My despair has started eating away at me,
Hopelessness is lending a hand.
The damp air I taste just makes me feel emptier,
Apart from that, I taste nothing.
My dirty rags are hardly enough to cover me.
It's so, so cold.
I can't bear it!
I look around at the gossiping maids,
At the other children trying to learn.
Any money at all?
I see the dark, dull shops,
I hear people calling to each other,
Then; *slam!*
There is nothing.

Polly Howarth (11)
Canonbury Primary School, Islington

My Life In 1906!

Out of the corner of my eye, a little girl, no younger than 5, is wheezing
breathlessly,
No one to love her, no one to care for her, just lying on the cobble steps, ill.
But what can I do? I'm no doctor!
Piles of dead, bloody animals cover the London streets,
Thankfully, strangely, children still play and have fun,
Bringing a little happiness into this world.
Sometimes, just sometimes, inside I feel unwanted, hopeless, useless, hungry.
I am scared for my whole family, worried for what the future holds.
My ears prick up because I hear shouting and crying.
But, laughter takes over the sadness and grief;
Everyone carries on with their life, regardless.
A bitter taste in my mouth makes a shiver run down my spine,
Wednesday's breakfast, that was three days ago!
My bitten nails catch the edge of my patchwork dress.
I feel comforted, I had proudly made it myself.
A sharp rock cuts deep into my foot.
I try to distract myself by smelling; the spices in the air,
The stench of the unwashed.
The dream I had when I was younger to be rich,
Have three meals a day,
Stand up for women's rights and be a doctor . . .
I've lost the will now.
By the time I'm twenty, I'll still be the same old Em,
Dreaming, hoping for more.

Sophie Trant-John (10)
Canonbury Primary School, Islington

Different

The life, the luxury, riding in gold carriages
The muck, the filth, living in the sewerage,
I look across the mud-ridden road,
Rats crawling around my bony ankles.
A tall, burly policeman strides into view,
A skinny pickpocket tries to take his gleaming whistle
Shadowed by a loyal mutt who scampers behind him,
Only stopping to sniff a rotting pigeon.
I slide out of view . . .
The life, the luxury, feeling fine,
The muck, the filth, being covered in grime.
My hand slides into my scratchy trouser pocket,
Searching helplessly for food.
I'm dizzy with hunger, so I follow the sign to the pie shop,
I close my eyes and breathe in.
The warm, fuzzy smell of the baking hot meat surrounds me,
Sending me to sleep. I open my eyes and look longingly through the window,
The baker stares back with disgust.
I feel like I'm classed as grime.
I get dizzier, my stomach's in a knot.
I fall asleep . . .
The life, the luxury, not knowing the fears,
The muck, the filth, gently crying your tears.
Why don't they like us, just because we're *different*?

Ruby Stevens (11)
Canonbury Primary School, Islington

The Rat

Rats scuttling along the floor, searching for scraps of food,
People selling anything they have just to keep alive,
Babies crying, children screaming,
Then, there's the cries of the rich people's drivers
Whipping the horses as the carriages swerve out of control,
Pickpockets stealing from the rich to save their own lives.
Me and the rat are alike,
Helpless, unwanted, lonely.

Max Weller (10)
Canonbury Primary School, Islington

The Disappointment

This lie;
I'm passing by, the viewer, staring down on her,
The disappointment,
The failure,
That's her, the little one with the scruffy hair . . .
All on her own.
Don't take pity on her, in a few days she'll be gone;
Taken by death, like the others.
She knows her fate,
She knows what's going to happen . . .
Death
The disappointment,
The failure.
The truth;
No family,
No house,
No food,
No money,
No school,
No life,
No hope.
That's me.
Death can take me.

Olivia Dugdale (10)
Canonbury Primary School, Islington

All Alone

The foul stench of rotting animals wafting towards my quivering nose.
I sniff the air trying desperately to pick out the aroma of food.
The gift of smell being one of my most useful senses.
A grand wooden carriage rattling along the cobbled streets.
Ever since I set eyes on one,
I dreamed that one day it would be me inside.

A shout from a gentleman snaps me out of my dream.
I listen, aware of muttering around me.
Me, a pointless piece of scum,
Just like all the others,
No one cares,
Me against the world.

My eyes follow a rat disappearing into the depths of an alleyway,
I might as well be that rat,
I am that rat.

I find myself in the sewers,
I trip and fall. I hardly notice the dirt anymore.
I can scarcely pay for food, let alone a nice wash.
My clothes are in tatters and scratch against my skin.
I have less hope now than I did when I began.

Rudi Wilmshurst (10)
Canonbury Primary School, Islington

Will My Life Go On This Way Forever?

Dirty, dead animals left lying on the street,
Poor, ragged, worn-out children, mourning for something to eat,
Starved with hunger,
My bones aching,
Will my life go on this way forever?

Grand women in carriages chatting away,
They look at me with disgust,
They never look back.

I dream of the future,
But I can't see it,
Clutching my brother,
The only thing I have left.

I dream that I'm rich,
Luxurious food,
A bed,
A home,
A place where I fit in,
But that's all a dream,
A fantasy,
It will never happen.

Ruth Tesfit (10)
Canonbury Primary School, Islington

39

Why Me?

My eyes ache with the scorching smoke
I'm finding it hard to breathe.
The blurred lines of unwanted children
Find their way to my brain.
I feel cut off, a sort of bond,
Broken, like a china doll.
My lack of confidence holds me back.
I want to help!
But, I can hardly support myself.

My rasping breath fills my ears,
But, the horses' hooves interfere.
The scratchy wicker basket clutched to my chest
Ugly brick walls trapping me like a prison.
My unwashed clothes, so covered with dust, no longer shows up the muck.
I wish my life hadn't started so badly, a mother who wouldn't leave me.
I've come to the point where I don't want to live.
Only my ambitions keep me going,
But, I don't know where they'll lead me.

Anna McAllister (11)
Canonbury Primary School, Islington

Filthy Vermin

Children sitting crying as their siblings try to comfort them,
Rats scurrying over my feet,
Men shouting,
Carriages skidding past me as if I'm not even there at all,
Pickpockets stealing men's pocket watches,
Rats scurrying into gutters,
Children trying to get every single penny they can get,
Posh people looking at us and thinking
Filthy vermin!

Samuel Cameron (10)
Canonbury Primary School, Islington

No Future

Cold, hungry, sad children, dirty, filthy vermin running over their feet,
Children selling firewood so they can earn a few pennies for their starving family,
I'm cold as ice, sick from hunger, there's no hope,
No future.
Dead animals rotting on the dirty streets, smoke from cooking fires, mud and
animal excrement all burning my nostrils.
I overhear rich women telling each other how disgusting we are, children crying,
selling things, shouting at people to buy wood, soup,
washing their clothes all for a few pennies.
I touch splintery wood, dirty rats brushing against my feet, I no longer jump,
A foul taste in my mouth from not eating, I run my tongue over my dirty teeth,
bad smells flowing into my mouth.
I hope a rich person will whisk me off in their carriage but I've stopped dreaming,
There's no hope,
No future.

Luella Knipe (10)
Canonbury Primary School, Islington

The Truth

Machine-gun bullets rattled past my head
Most of the troops in my regiment dead
All of our boats are homing in on shore
We are gonna make England proud for sure
Corpses litter all the French battle land
Best friend's body detached from his hand
Spitfires flock the air overhead
Tears of sad families are being shed
As the battle draws to a final close
The pain and exhaustion of the troops shows
Thousands of brave soldiers dead for one land
Never should this onslaught be brought upon man.

Kai Robinson (11)
Goffs Oak Primary School, Waltham Cross

War Is . . .

Rattling turrets pumping out ammo,
Shells primed and ready to blow.
Young men falling all around,
Carcasses littering the war torn ground.

Fires raging, floating ash
Mixing with the poisonous gas.
Shrapnel flying through the air
Everyone fighting, all is unfair.

Tanks and buggies lining the hill,
Weapons aimed and fired, meant to kill!
Blazing aircraft as hot as the hearth,
Crashing and tearing up the earth.

People crying in despair,
Wishing their loved ones were still there.
Families are suffering too,
Hoping for the best and wondering what to do.

Bombing is occurring overnight,
People are going mad with fright!
A mighty empire is turning into dust,
Yet in with our soldiers we must trust.

The English flag flying high,
Almost seeming to touch the sky.
The soldier's war-cry rings out loud,
The troops doing their country proud.

Thomas Watson (11)
Goffs Oak Primary School, Waltham Cross

The Smelly Streets

The sounds of small rat's feet
Running up and down the street
See workhouses tall and mean
See the small beggars tiny and lean.

Cries from the factories
Almost deafen me
Petrified chimney sweeps
I can hear their weeps.

Mud plunges into the dark mines
The miners are trapped inside
Shouting, crying, probably dying
I feel like running and hiding.

Rich people pushing all around me
I fell clumsily and cut my knee
I got up and turned sharply around
And spotted a market stall with bread for a pound.

I gobbled up the bread hungrily
I turned around and right before me
Was a splendid, shining horse and cart
It was an amazing piece of art.

Lottie Lee (10)
Goffs Oak Primary School, Waltham Cross

A Typical Victorian Life

There are filthy, unhygienic rats
Running across the streets
And all you can hear is some high-pitched screaming
From the chimney sweeps
It's all because they're not fast enough
And their masters can sometimes be tough
One light of that terrifying log
The chimney fills up with horrid fog
Burn, burn, burn, burn, burn, burn
That's how the kids have to learn
I hear a loud bang as someone is hanged
I give a scream; a killer gives a suspicious gleam
People glare and people stare
I begin to feel really scared
What if I had a death like that?
I'd rather be killed by killer rats
This is life, I know it's mean
It's like a big drama scene.

Emma Lamberti (10)
Goffs Oak Primary School, Waltham Cross

Volatile Victorians

The colossal rats crawl up my leg
As I watch people sit and beg
I can hear the chimney sweeps' yelps from far away
And I'm watching kids jump happily in the hay
The horses got very angry and bucked
Well, all I'm saying is that it's not their luck
The dirt is falling off the factory walls
And I can hear people inside, terrible calls
Deafening gas is spreading fast
Now let's hope it will not last.

Macey Salmon (10)
Goffs Oak Primary School, Waltham Cross

The Workhouse

Inside the workhouse it's wicked and cruel
I am petrified of all the terrifying rules.
Inside the workhouse, out came the cane
We all hoped we wouldn't receive the pain.
Whilst we ate I felt a shiver down my spine
Someone's hand is going to be caned,
Maybe mine!
The master begins to speak very stern
And that is how we have to learn.

Lily Marriage (10)
Goffs Oak Primary School, Waltham Cross

Vile Victorians

The filthy rats crawl up my legs
As my hands shake and beg
The smelly streets are full of dirt
You have to be very alert.

All the chimney sweepers get burnt
Their master wouldn't mind if they were hurt
All the sweepers would shout and scream
And they wouldn't be very keen.

Abigail O'Donnell (10)
Goffs Oak Primary School, Waltham Cross

The Victorian Workhouse

The petrifying workhouse which fills everyone with dread
We would rather have two up, two down and a comfy bed
The cruel, wicked master watching our every move
Whipped when I tripped because I have no soles on my worn shoes
My soft, awkward, slurred speech slowly falls from my tasteless mouth
I'm trying not to shed a tear from my sad, lifeless eyes
Horrifying scents are surrounding, wafting up my nose
Disgusting, poor conditions with dirt that sticks to my clothes.

Gemma Backman (10)
Goffs Oak Primary School, Waltham Cross

Living In Fear

In the dirty, revolting Victorian street
See those colossal, unhygienic rats
Terrifying, volatile beggars hanging about
With the picky pickpockets running around
Take a look inside the Victorian workhouse
See the painful cane creeping out
All the poor children creeping around
Trying to keep from being hurt.

Leah Gill (10)
Goffs Oak Primary School, Waltham Cross

Destruction Of Pompeii

What can you see?
Lava streaming down and rocks shooting out
Horses and cats running away
Rocks landing, dogs barking,
Children and babies screaming,
People shouting for help,
The ground shaking,
I am the only one here.

What can I hear?
Rocks crashing, *boom!*
Lava behind you,
People screaming for help.
The volcano erupting,
Dogs barking, cats running away,
Girls screaming,
Buildings falling over, people shouting,
Horses running away from Vesuvius.

What can you feel?
Rocks bashing behind you, *boom, boom, boom!*
Lava swishing behind you, *whoosh, whoosh, whoosh!*
Volcanoes going *boom!*
I feel my heart racing.

James Lancaster (7)
Highover JMI School, Hitchin

Inventions

Victorian times

Many things were invented in
Victorian times

The camera
Victorian times

The X-ray
Victorian times

The first railway
Victorian times

The bright dyes for clothes
Victorian times

The Singer sewing machine
Victorian times

The first aeroplane
Victorian times

The telegraph
Victorian times

The photograph paper
Victorian times

The typewriter
Victorian times

The vacuum cleaner
Victorian times

The telephone
Victorian times

The penny black stamp
Victorian times

The toilet
Victorian times

Hooray for Victorian times!

Liberty Canavan (10)
Highover JMI School, Hitchin

Destruction Of Pompeii

What can you see?
I can see rocks falling on the ground,
Hot lava sliding down and up,
Boats sailing away quickly,
Crushed people.

What can you hear?
Pets barking loudly,
People shouting for help,
Big bang,
Windows smashing.

What can you feel?
Lava between my feet,
Smoke coming towards me,
Ash sliding down near me,
Rocks shooting up and hitting me.

What can you feel?
Terrified and upset,
Scared and frightened,
Shocked and upset,
Poor because I've lost everything.

Zarish Majeed (7)
Highover JMI School, Hitchin

Destruction Of Pompeii

What can you see?
A volcano can kill people because it has poisonous gases.
A volcano destroys people's lives.
A volcano has massive rocks.
A volcano explodes like a firework.
A volcano has hot ash coming down.
A volcano shoots out rocks.
A volcano has a magma chamber.
A volcano has a hole.

Megan Brundell (8)
Highover JMI School, Hitchin

Nursery Girl

Rock, rock, rock
I ride you every day
In the nursery I play
My head aches because the babies cry
I'm lonely as there's no one to play with
Wish I was galloping in the fields
Squeak, creak, creak

I wobble all the time
Will I slip off?
I comb your hard mane tidily
And stroke your painted nose
I plait your tail like my hair
Gallop, trot, stop

Nursery maid said it's time for my tea
Eat my tea quickly
So I can ride my horse
But it had been put away!
Oh no!

Nicole Buckley (9)
Highover JMI School, Hitchin

Children At Work

Chimney to chimney, high I climb,
But I have to risk my life,
I have to taste lots of grime,
Chimney to chimney, high I climb.

Deep, deep underground,
I have to drag coal and I can hardly get out,
The pain is bad but I am proud,
Deep, deep underground.

Watch out, watch out, I am near,
Pockets I have to clear,
Since my master I do fear,
Watch out, watch out, I am near!

Jamie Oliver-Rocha (9)
Highover JMI School, Hitchin

Destruction Of Pompeii

What can you see?
People are running.
Babies are crying.
Some people are covering in black and grey dust.
People are screaming.
Hot, sticky lava is falling on dogs, pets and humans.
The windows are breaking.
Dogs are barking, people are dying.

What can you hear?
People calling for help.
Houses are cracking.
Lava is splashing in the hot sea.
People are running,
Their feet are tapping on the hard, hot road.
People praying for death to the gods.

What can you feel?
My heart is racing inside my body.
The Earth is shaking.
Hot, sticky lava is falling on me.
What's happening? I don't know.

Hannah Bellamy (7)
Highover JMI School, Hitchin

Destruction Of Pompeii

People crying for help, babies crying their eyes out.
The world shaking people are frightened.
People are starting to think that it is the end of the world.
Boats sailing away, people are screaming for free boats.

What can you see?
People crying for help, pets are very scared.
The world shaking, people are frightened.
People are starting to think that they are going to die.
Bombs exploding boats ruined.

What can you hear?
People's hearts beating faster and faster.
Screaming and screaming for help.
People dying, people screaming.
People trying to be quiet.

What can you feel?
People shaking, people having surgery.
People's hearts racing along.
People are starting to fall blind.
People's hands breaking, people's legs breaking.

Riyad Ali (8)
Highover JMI School, Hitchin

51

Destruction Of Pompeii

What can you see?
Rocks hitting the ground.
The Earth shaking.
People running, people dying.
Lava pea drops sizzling down on people.
Houses falling down.
Buildings breaking and cracking.

What can you hear?
People screaming for help
And trying to recognise their voices.
Big rocks coming down like boulders too.
Babies and pets barking and crying.
Kaboom, kaboom, loudly as can be.

What can you feel?
Hot rocks banging down on people's heads.
Sea as hot as a fire.
Burning lava under people's feet, burning their shoes.

Denver Parris (7)
Highover JMI School, Hitchin

Victorian

The Queen was called Victoria,
She ruled the world for 64 years,
I live in the world she ruled,
I come from a very rich family,
My whole family is rich,
I live in a big house,
My gran ruled the world,
I go to visit my gran, she lives in Buckingham Palace,
My mother says if I concentrate and study
I will be like my gran.
My gran buys me a lot of toys
I have a lot of dolls and they look so pretty,
So have you guessed who I am?
I am Queen Elizabeth the second.

Rammeja Anantharajah (9)
Highover JMI School, Hitchin

Destruction Of Pompeii

What can you see?
I can see lava coming out of the volcano
And rocks shooting in the sky.
They need to go but the boats have gone
I am the last one here.

What can you hear?
I can hear babies crying
A big boom as well
Dogs barking, this is a lot of noise
But it is quiet now
Nobody knows where they have gone.

What can you feel?
I can feel burning rocks crashing on me
And ash too.
I can feel lava dripping on me
And I feel like a boiled egg.
It is so hot, I feel devastated.
It is the end of the world.

Poppy Rochfort (7)
Highover JMI School, Hitchin

Destruction Of Pompeii

What can you see?
Hot lava raining down the volcano like a nasty firestorm.
Houses cracking, rocks smacking.
A mountain exploding, sizzling like mad.
Smoky ash covering Pompeii, everything is black.

What can you hear?
People yelling for help, volcanoes shouting *kaboom!*
Rumbling thunder, wind blowing, windows smashing.
Babies crying, everyone screaming like they will never stop.
Bubbles from the sea popping, lava crackling and pets barking.

What can you feel?
Yucky red blood touching my foot on the floor,
Rocks hitting my front door.
Absolutely devastated because my loved ones have been killed.
The Earth shaking, my heart racing.
I am really frightened because the boats have sailed away,
I don't know what to do!

Louise Harris (7)
Highover JMI School, Hitchin

The Victorians

Many Victorians were very poor,
Their houses were small with a tattered floor.
There was little water so they couldn't wash,
Except for the rich people who were posh.
Life for Victorian children was hard,
They had no garden or even a yard.
Victorian children often missed school,
They couldn't play games or even play pool.
They worked in factories, risked losing a leg,
Or went up chimneys or out on the streets to beg.
There were lots of inventors good at knowing,
How to make machines for typing and sewing.
Living with Victorians was not very nice,
Everywhere was smelly and overrun with mice.

James Keshishian (9)
Highover JMI School, Hitchin

Destruction Of Pompeii

What can you see?
I can see Mount Vesuvius exploding.
I can see people running and jumping over the lava.
I can see boats sailing away as quickly as they can.
I can see dust-covered people.

What can you hear?
I can hear people crying for help.
I can hear pets crying.
I can even hear the boats.
I can hear houses crashing and bashing together.

What can you feel?
I can feel ash hitting at my feet but I'm kicking it off.
I also feel terrified because my house has fallen down
And I don't know where to live.
I can feel my bones shaking.
I can also feel the lava trying to push the ash to me
And I don't know what to do.

Emily Peter (7)
Highover JMI School, Hitchin

Destruction Of Pompeii

What can you see?
I can see Mount Vesuvius exploding.
Smoky ash rocks dashing down from the volcano.
People screaming and running, pets barking.

What can you hear?
People crying for help.
They think that it is the end of the world.
Lava touching my feet and my legs.
I can hear the volcano shaking and shaking.

What can you feel?
I can feel the ground shaking.
My heart feels like it will never beat again.
I am very burning hot and tired.

Jessica Horton (7)
Highover JMI School, Hitchin

Destruction Of Pompeii

What can you see?
The giant mountain destroying Pompeii.
All the boats sailing away from shore,
People screaming for help.
The poisonous gases, ash escaping from Vesuvius.

What can you hear?
Vesuvius erupting, people shouting for help.
Vesuvius made a *kaboom* sound,
It spread a sort of gas.
Lava raining down, making a sound
That a stove makes when something is burning.

What can you feel?
Frustrated because the Pompeii people
Think they did something wrong.
Shocked because they do not know what a volcano is.
Upset because they do not know why this mountain has erupted.

Ranata Mudaly (7)
Highover JMI School, Hitchin

Destruction Of Pompeii

What can you see?
People running as fast as they can.
Everything is turning into dusty rock.
Loud firestorms happening.
Shooting rocks coming out of Vesuvius.
What can you hear?
People shouting for help.
Windows smashing, *bang*.
Things going *kaboom!*
Babies crying.
What can you feel?
Sweat on me.
My heart beating fast.
Heat of the red lava.
Hard rocks.

Dilani Arulampalam (7)
Highover JMI School, Hitchin

Destruction Of Pompeii

What can you see?
Land moving and the floor shaking.
Houses breaking, horses running.
People running away, frightened of the volcano.

What can you hear?
I can hear the volcano shaking.
I can hear houses shaking.
I can hear people running from the hot ash.
I can hear trees falling down.

What can you feel?
I feel sad because people are running.
I feel mad.
People are getting hurt.
I am upset.
I am scared.
I am hurt.

Heather Basak (7)
Highover JMI School, Hitchin

Destruction Of Pompeii

What can you see?
A mountain erupting and Pompeii falling apart.
Dogs barking while running away and houses falling apart.
Boats floating away in the hot sea.
Trees burning and swaying side to side.

What can you hear?
Big rocks crashing. Cracks in the ground shaking.
Smoke coming like little raindrops hitting the floor.
People screaming, babies crying.
Boats creaking while falling down the earthquake hole.

What can you feel?
Lava burning my legs as I'm running.
Giant rocks crashing right on me.
I feel so frightened because it is the end of the world.

George Brown (7)
Highover JMI School, Hitchin

The Destruction Of Pompeii

What can you see?
Lava rock and lava ball blasting out of the top of the volcano.
Boats floating away and buildings falling down.
I can see orange bubbles.

What can you hear?
A mountain exploding, Pompeii destroyed.
I would hear lava shooting out of the top.
I would hear people screaming really loudly because Vesuvius is erupting badly.
I can hear crying for help and people dying.

What can you feel?
I can feel lava rumbling and the ground shaking.
Hot rocks bursting out of the volcano.
A covering sand burning us.
Volcano bursting out on us people, just lying there, dead.
It's the end of the world.

Jamie Bissett (7)
Highover JMI School, Hitchin

Destruction Of Pompeii

What can you see?
A mountain going to erupt and destroy Pompeii.
People running, people going to boats, people dying, people suffocating.
Dark grey ash spreading around trying to catch you.
The sky is black, the ground is red, all you can see is black and red.

What can you hear?
People screaming, shouting, boats paddling, houses crashing.
Hearts racing.
Thunderstorms happening, the wind blowing ash in people's faces.
The lava sizzling, the rocks crashing down, making cracks on the ground.

What can you feel?
Pompeii shaking, bits breaking, ash covering everything around you.
Hot lava chasing you, just going to catch you.
Hard, bumpy rocks following you like rain but faster.
Sea burning the boats and fishes melting.

Kiertan Sangha (7)
Highover JMI School, Hitchin

Destruction Of Pompeii

What can you see?
I can see red-hot, sticky lava.
I can see people running away from Vesuvius.
I can see people getting killed.
I can see the boats sailing away.

What can you hear?
I can hear a baby crying.
I can hear people gasping.
I can hear a dog barking.
I can hear a cat miaowing.

What can you feel?
I can feel a cat.
I can feel a dog.
I can feel my mum.
I cannot feel my sister and Dad and Joshua.

Alex Kovacevic (7)
Highover JMI School, Hitchin

Destruction Of Pompeii

What can you see?
I can see the lava raining down.
People running for their lives.
I see boats on fire and boats sailing away.
Smoking houses and burning buildings.

What can you hear?
I can hear children crying, some babies dying.
People shaking.
Lava flowing down and houses falling.
I can hear *kaboom*.

What can you feel?
The Earth shaking.
Hot, sticky lava.
Hot, red, sticky blood.
Choking ash falling like rain.

Hamzah Malik (7)
Highover JMI School, Hitchin

Destruction Of Pompeii

What can you see?
Boats burning up,
Crumbling,
Boats sailing away,
Vesuvius exploding in Pompeii.

What can you hear?
Dogs barking and people shouting.
Vesuvius erupting.
Houses coming down.
People shouting, people running.

What can you feel?
Ground shaking.
Feels like it is the end of the world.
Heart racing.
Hot lava burning.

Merlin Shelford-Clarke (7)
Highover JMI School, Hitchin

Destruction Of Pompeii

What can you see?
The ground moving and people screaming.
Smoky ash covering the place.
Everything is black.
I can see hot lava raining down.

What can you hear?
I can hear hot water flowing.
Boiling lava splashing.
I can hear windows smashing and houses falling down.
I can hear rocks bursting out of the volcano.

What can you feel?
I can feel choking ash falling like rain.
I can feel my heart racing through my body.
I can feel pea drops of lava all over.
It's like the end of the world.

Nathan Collinson (8)
Highover JMI School, Hitchin

Destruction Of Pompeii

What can you see?
The volcano has lava flowing towards Pompeii.
The volcano has ash falling on the people of Pompeii.
The volcano has rocks shooting towards the town of Pompeii.
A mountain exploding, Pompeii's destruction.

What can you hear?
A volcano going *kaboom* and a rumbling volcano.
A volcano erupting and lava flowing.
A volcano going *kaboom* and rocks crashing.
A volcano erupting, a house tumbling down.

What can you feel?
Hot rocks burning behind me.
The heat from the red, fiery lava.
The shaking of a volcano.
The volcano shaking.

Samuel James (8)
Highover JMI School, Hitchin

Destruction Of Pompeii

What can you see?
Vesuvius exploding, Pompeii being destroyed, everyone running in fear.
A firestorm coming, Mount Vesuvius erupting, people running in fear.
Someone running while Vesuvius is erupting, red-hot lava behind,
While Vesuvius explodes, some ash and molten rock.

What can you hear?
Crying babies, people screaming like it's the end of Italy.
A big kaboom, when a house comes crashing down like it's the end.
Everyone screaming and lava splashing, rocks crashing down,
Like it's the end of the world, people ducking like it's the end.

What can you feel?
Lava flowing and everyone getting going, everyone covered in ash,
People of Pompeii screaming in fear, hearts racing for safety.
Lava killing people, everyone crying and lots of suffocation.
Everyone praying for salvation, like it's the end.

Tyler Walker (7)
Highover JMI School, Hitchin

61

Destruction Of Pompeii

What can you see?
Boats on fire and horses running
I see a volcano erupting
Everybody running away from burning red-hot lava.

What can you hear?
I can hear people shouting
I can hear buildings booming
I can hear pets going mad
Because they are frightened.

What can you feel?
The lava is so hot
The ashes falling like rain
I feel scared
I am angry.

Luke Reid (7)
Highover JMI School, Hitchin

Destruction Of Pompeii

What can you see?
Vesuvius was erupting, the boats were gone
People had nowhere to go, some people were running
I would see hot lava flowing
Rocks falling out of the sky
Houses breaking, smoke going everywhere, everything is black.

What can you hear?
Babies crying, people screaming, dogs shouting
Buildings crashing and splashing, big kaboom, people screaming,
Help, rocks crashing down.

What can you feel?
Rocks slide, people running, yucky red blood,
Hot sea, hot, sticky lava,
Hard bumpy rocks.

Raheim Saddler (7)
Highover JMI School, Hitchin

Destruction Of Pompeii

What can you see?
I can see a gigantic mountain going to erupt.
The ground moving, people suffocating from it.
Boats are sinking, melting, lava popping out of the water.
People screaming for help for their family and friends.

What can you hear?
I can hear children shouting for help, houses collapsing, cracking.
Windows smashing, dogs barking like maniacs.
Earthquakes rumbling, sizzling lava.
Babies crying like it's the end of the world.

What can you feel?
I can feel burning hot lava and rocks hitting me.
I can feel hot fire, burning hot blood,
Poisonous gases exploding.

Xavier Alleyne (7)
Highover JMI School, Hitchin

A Poor Tudor

A poor Tudor house
Would have a hole in the wall for a window
Where they all lived in a room with a mouse
And shared their sorrow

They had to sleep on straw beds
And had small blankets
To keep them warm at times
For the lack of good socks and jackets

They always felt sad and hungry
Suffered from the rich and made them angry
They were punished for begging
And had a bad life ending

The poor had to work hard
And struggled to survive
They had all kinds of disease
And lived up to the age of thirty-five.

Thomas Saliba (8)
Leopold Primary School, Willesden

Victorian England

In Victorian England I can see:
Horses walking by,
Children sweeping chimneys all day long,
Flower girls selling flowers,
Street urchins walking past,
Servants looking after rich families,
Teachers using the cane to cane children,
Children washing clothes,
Adults and children working in factories
And also street urchins looking for new families.

In Victorian England I can hear:
Horses trotting down the pathway,
Flower girls shouting, 'Buy my flowers please!'
The sound of wind floating by,
Children shouting,
The clock ticking to 12,
The bell ringing for the cemetery,
Children running to get to the cemetery.

In Victorian England I can feel:
Sad children working in dangerous places,
Getting caned by the teachers,
Wearing the dunce cap,
Climbing up chimneys,
Going down mines,
Getting hurt in dangerous factories.

Litchina Krya McKenzie (10)
Leopold Primary School, Willesden

64

A Poor Tudor

There wasn't anything that showed the gap more
Than what rich and poor people were wearing.
Shimmering gold brocade and sparkling jewels
For the rich and famous, putting them in a different class.
Plain and simple clothes for the common mass.
It was an uphill battle working towards the brass.

Tudor people had hard, often short lives,
Usually affected by poor diets.
Living in homes that were not kept clean,
Surviving was their dream.
Adults and children were infected,
Not much medicine to be selected.

Tudors were struggling in degrading conditions to survive,
The men working as labourers and craftsmen,
Hoping to make a better life.
Thinking of their underprivileged children and wives,
Nothing could stop them carrying on the fight.

Kia Mensah
Leopold Primary School, Willesden

In Victorian England

The smell of horse pat
And the bakery
That's what it's like in Victorian England
That's what it's like in Victorian England
The rich people putting their noses up
To us poor street urchins
People buying sweets and cakes
Which we can't afford
That's what it's like in Victorian England
That's what it's like in Victorian England
They have the latest fashion
They have cars and dolls,
That's what they have.
Which we can't afford.

Genie-Jo (9)
Leopold Primary School, Willesden

In Victorian England

In Victorian England . . .
I can see chimney sweeps, people selling and people begging,
I can see windmills, scraps and factories,
I can see rich people, poor people and everybody,
I can see washing wells and people eating their tea.

In Victorian England . . .
I can hear thinking of people here and there,
I can hear children screaming with fear,
I can hear the canes swishing in teachers' palms,
I can hear the reading of children reading a scripture from Psalms.

In Victorian England . . .
I can feel pain of children,
I can feel the warmth from the fire,
I can feel the fear, the crying of young children,
I can feel the people getting carriages for hire.

Cleo Rose Stern (10)
Leopold Primary School, Willesden

A Poor Tudor

What I see:
Boils and sores are causing tears
But watered ale eases my fears,
After the vegetable harvest that we reap and sow,
We plant the wheat and watch it grow.

What I feel:
After working on the farm all day,
The money I get is very little pay,
This makes me angry and distressed,
Which makes me even more depressed.

What I hear:
I hear the children singing ring-a-ring o' roses,
So I carry a pocket full of posies.
The singing is better than the cries I hear
When I pass the dungeons, this I can hear.

Jason Mauricette Rammsamy (8)
Leopold Primary School, Willesden

66

A Poor Tudor's Tale

Out of the small window the sun shone in,
Smoke climbed up to the roof from the central fire within,
In the corner there stood the smelly animals grazing their food.

It feels cold, damp and I am so hungry,
My stomach feels empty and there is no food,
There is never any food in the poor Tudor home.

I wait outside the manor house hoping for the scraps to be thrown,
There on the dusty ground,
I find an old crust of bread and gulp this down.

Suddenly I hear loud cries from afar,
A large crowd had gathered in the village for a show.
A poor Tudor is being punished for nagging in the town,
The people chant and shout,
I feel sad and wish that my life wouldn't always be so bad.

Milla Rose (8)
Leopold Primary School, Willesden

Victorian England

In Victorian England I can hear big old bells,
Lots of people shouting so loud,
Lovely horses going *clip-clop, clip-clop,*
I can hear the brush of sweeps sweeping the rusty chimneys,
And scraps of old newspaper rolling on the ground in the wind.

In Victorian England I can see lots of kind street urchins,
Very quiet road sweepers,
Young, lovely, kind girls being servants,
Lots of angry people waiting in the line to dry their clothes.

In Victorian England I feel very sad that I am a child
who has to work,
I can feel the painful cane that the teacher uses,
And feeling embarrassed wearing the dunce's hat.

Keleisha Innswood (9)
Leopold Primary School, Willesden

In Victorian England!

I can see chimney sweeps and water pumps,
The poor children with excitement they can't jump,
They end up with a bump,
Flower sellers, horses and rich people with their dogs.

I can hear horses galloping down the road,
And ugly, vile people looking like toads,
Bells ringing like crazy and the clocks ticking, *tick-tock!*
And last of all, the wind whizzing past us.

I can feel the hard, cold dunce's cap on my head for my stupidity,
And the cane that feels like you're sat on steel,
Being whiplashed against your great big bottom,
And the slate boards and pencils that made your hands feel numb,
Like you were injected.

Victoria Peacock (9)
Leopold Primary School, Willesden

A Poor Tudor

I can see by the bustle in the square
It's market day today
I really crave the food my eyes are eating in dismay
The pork pies sparkle in the sun like jewels in the King's crown
But only the rich folk, bellies large, taste the best food in my town.

I can feel my anger and frustration rising in my blood
As I rummage through the rotten and discarded food lying in the mud
I'm so hungry I could eat a hundred tons of meat and bread
My shrunken tummy wants something yummy, it's dying to be fed.

Rustle, bustle, rustle, bustle, people everywhere
Horses neighing, babies screaming, dogs barking very near
Chitter-chatter, laughing, talking, coins rattling in the air
But the loudest sound is my rumbling tummy in the market square.

Felix Stodart (8)
Leopold Primary School, Willesden

A Poor Tudor

What can you see?
People working really hard, struggling to survive
In their villages doing farm work or making cloth
In their homes for very little pay
It was very tempting to steal food when harvest failed

What can you feel?
Very hungry because we have no food
And are treated badly by the rich Tudors.

What can you hear?
Lots of singing and dancing
And Tudors going to the theatres and having fun
The rich had time for falconry, hunting, jousting,
Tennis and bowls.

Shauntay McKenzie-Maxwell (8)
Leopold Primary School, Willesden

Pearl The Tudor Girl

Poor little Tudor girl,
Who goes by the name of Pearl,
She goes to Wycome Earl
And sits in the corner alone.

She smells like a rotten egg going to explode,
Pearl is so tiny, she cannot lift a heavy load,
Her hands are as rough as elephant's skin,
And her nails are as sharp as an opened tin.

Pearl is as small and quiet as a mouse,
Who lives in the corner of a great big house,
She's as scruffy as a rug,
But she longs for a big hug.

Serena Azu (8)
Leopold Primary School, Willesden

In Victorian England

Children sweep scraps from the ground,
The clock arrow spins round and round.
Children at school are not heard,
Not even a noise from a bird.

The mum and dad sleep in their bed,
Some children are misled.
Children sometimes live on the street,
When it is hot they feel the heat.

Lots of noise from falling blocks,
Children are stepping on hard rocks.
They all live in town,
Some children make a frown.

Paul Earle Jnr (9)
Leopold Primary School, Willesden

Victorian Poem

In Victorian England I can see
Street urchins and carriages parking.
I can see teachers using canes
And children crying in pain.
I can see children getting water,
People just eating a quarter.
I can hear bells ringing like people singing.
I can hear people shouting and people selling.
I can feel fires burning hot,
I can feel hot water in a pot.
I can feel a cold breeze,
That makes me feel that I am going to freeze.

Ta-Jaun Subaran (10)
Leopold Primary School, Willesden

In Victorian England

I can hear horses trotting along the road,
Vile people shouting,
People yelling
When they are selling.
Clocks chiming,
The sound of children screaming after being whipped by the cane,
People's footsteps.

In Victorian England I can see
Rich women,
Flower sellers, servants and street urchins,
Windmills,
Children working or going to school,
Numerous shops.

In Victorian England I can feel
The dirty water, the pain of the cane,
The flowers the flower sellers sell.

Kainaat Niazi (10)
Leopold Primary School, Willesden

Tudor Wars

Who has seen the Tudors?
Neither I nor you,
But when the bombs land,
The wind is pushing through.

The Tudors were fighting,
Even though half were dying.
They didn't really care because their friends were lying.
The Tudors were flying even though they were crying.

The Tudors had heard the aeroplane crashing
The Tudors had heard the aeroplane crashing
The Tudors had screamed when they heard the Vikings shouting.

Anthony O'Brien (9)
Leopold Primary School, Willesden

Victorian England

In Victorian England I can see,
Teachers using the cane immediately,
I can also see horses that are tame.
In Victorian England I can hear,
The whack of the cane which may be severe.
In Victorian England I can feel,
The straining of the machine hurting my spleen.

Erran Boyle O'Brien (9)
Leopold Primary School, Willesden

Victorian England

Well! Victorian England, where do I begin?
The children there are so thin.

In Victorian England you can see
Little boys swiping soot from chimneys.

In Victorian England you can feel
The whip of a teacher's cane
What a sound to your ears, the pain.
Some people would say it's insane,
Just thinking of little children in pain.

Catriona Ansha Ison (9)
Leopold Primary School, Willesden

Victorian

In Victorian England I can see people going to school
I can see people washing their clothes
I can see people getting caned in their school.

I can hear bells ringing
I hear horses trotting up the road
I can hear the sound of the wind

I can feel the sadness of children having to work
I can feel the heat of the heater
I can feel the cold wind.

Jayden Daniel Michael (9)
Leopold Primary School, Willesden

A Poor Tudor

I can see rich Tudors laughing at me
It was dangerous out on the street
It was smelly as a skunk
I could hear mean cackling
I ran dangerously
I could taste sweet-smelling food
I could touch the hard street
I was like a flower with power
But what would happen to me?

Ki-Ran Grenville (8)
Leopold Primary School, Willesden

Poor Tudor

In the old, smelly streets
There's a Tudor walking pleased
In the old, smelly streets
I can hardly ever eat
People begging for their money
But if you do, off and get the chop
Through prickly, tarmac streets
Glass bottles scattered around
And horses going *neigh, neigh.*

Ahmed Galgal (8)
Leopold Primary School, Willesden

A Poor Tudor

A poor Tudor is as busy as a bee
Never sits down, always around
They're all in such a hurry just to get money
Mice and rats run upon your feet when walking

Looking in shops but can't buy anything
They're all sad, never happy
Fighting for money and a better life
Maybe all the fighting will change their lives.

Nadim Elakhal (8)
Leopold Primary School, Willesden

The Battle Of Bosworth

When Richard became king,
Henry hated that with a fling.
He landed in Wales to give him a bash,
The swords hit each other, their helmets crashed.
They watched out for spears which could cut out their ears,
They carried shields so they wouldn't be killed.
Richard came charging, crashing Henry's troops.
He got knocked off his horse, by a battling knight
That he met one night, before the fight.

Joseph Leo Kituku (8)
Northside Primary School, North Finchley

The Boat Is Chugging Forward

The boat is going slowly
But the waves are whipping fast
The boat is chugging forward
France is creeping up at last

The spray of the sea is singing
Ringing in my ear
The boat is chugging forward
France is very near

I try to act quite brave
But I'm still a young 18
The boat is chugging forward
It is France that now I see

The boat arrives at the beach
My heart is pounding loud
The boat is chugging forward
But the other way now

I'm stranded on the beach
Though the crew is all around me
The boat is chugging forward
Out to sea

Boom, boom, boom
The machine-gun goes
It cuts through my body
Till it reaches my heart

Slowly I fall, tears trickling
And I think about my mum
The way she kissed me
She is my mum
But I'm not her son.

Jack Medlin (10)
Northside Primary School, North Finchley

Napoleon Bonaparte
(15th August 1769 – 5th May 1821)

After the French Revolution of 1789 had overthrown King Louis XVI, Napoleon rose to power rapidly - he was a military genius with a brilliant command.

He was a short man, with the nickname 'the little corporal'. His rise to power was helped by his first wife, the beautiful Josephine de Beauharnais.

After bringing economic prosperity and peace to France, Napoleon set out to conquer the remainder of Europe. He was able to conquer a significant amount of land.

In 1804 Napoleon crowned himself emperor of the French and received the Pope's blessing.

Today Napoleon has a chess move named after him: the 'Napoleon Opening'.

Napoleon was finally defeated in June 1815 at Waterloo. Napoleon surrendered and was exiled on the small island of St Helena.

Joan of Arc

(1412 – 30th May 1431)

Joan of Arc is the youngest person in history to command the armies of a nation. Charles VII officially gave Joan command of the armies of France when she was only 17.

A prophecy foretold that France would be saved by a maid from Lorraine. It was a popular prediction in France during Joan's time and has been attributed to prophets including the mythical Merlin.

Joan of Arc's greatest military victory was at Patay on June 18th, 1429. Joan's army annihilated the English force, killing over 2,000 while suffering almost no losses.

Charles himself drew Joan's coat of arms featuring a sword holding a crown with a fleur-de-lis on each side.

Joan predicted she would be wounded by an arrow in her chest during an attack on the fort Les Tourelles. Her prediction came true and is documented in a letter written by Charles' cousin fifteen days before.

Joan of Arc was officially canonized by Pope Benedict XV on May 16th 1920, under the same church that executed her for heresy.

Vikings
(The late 8th to the mid 11th century)

The name 'Viking' means 'a pirate raid' in the Old Norse language.

The Vikings were famous for sailing huge distances. Around 500 years before Christopher Columbus 'discovered' the Americas, Vikings had visited their shores. Leif Ericsson was the one who led the Vikings over to what is now Canada in around AD 1000.

Among the many gods Vikings believed in were Thor, the god of thunder, and Loki, a cheeky mischief-maker who could shape-shift to become all different kinds of animals.

The Vikings were expert boat builders and sailors. They invented 'keels' which made their 'longboats' easy to steer, and because of their design to float high in the water, landing on beaches was easy.

Fenrir Greyback, the werewolf in the Harry Potter books, was named after a ferocious giant wolf from Ancient Viking mythology.

Vegetables in Viking times were much smaller than the ones we enjoy today, they were more like wild plants. Viking carrots were dark purple, not orange!

Victorians

(Queen Victoria's reign lasted from 20th June 1837 until her death on 22nd January 1901)

Britain became the most powerful and richest country in the world, with the largest empire that had ever existed, ruling a quarter of the world's population.

Britain built a huge empire during the Victorian period. In 1837 most people lived in villages and worked on the land; by 1901, most lived in towns and worked in offices, shops and factories.

The number of people living in Britain more than doubled from 16 million to 37 million, causing a huge demand for food, clothes and housing.

There were no painkillers nor anaesthesia for the Victorians - operations went on for hours with patients in excruciating agony.

The police force was created during the Victorian period by Sir Robert Peel (hence the nickname 'Bobbies').

To control insects, many people kept a hedgehog in the basement. It curled up and slept in the day, but roamed around the dark kitchen at night eating cockroaches and other insects.

Children were often forced to work. Many were used as cheap labour in factories, or as chimney sweeps. The work was dangerous and painful. Some boys got stuck and died of suffocation.

Henry VIII & Tudors

**(Henry's reign 28th June 1491 – 28th January 1547
Tudor dynasty from 1485 until 1603)**

The first Tudor king was Henry VII. He became king after the Battle of Bosworth Field, which ended the Wars of the Roses.

Henry VIII is probably the most well known of the Tudor monarchs. He was a very selfish person and by the end of his life everyone was afraid of him, mainly because of his ruthless behaviour toward anyone who didn't agree with him.

In 1534, Henry VIII broke away from the Catholic Church and proclaimed himself head of the Church of England. Henry sold off the land and riches of the church to dukes, barons and other noblemen.

Contrary to popular opinion, Henry VIII had many children. Unfortunately it was very common in Tudor times for them to die very young. Only three survived beyond childhood.

An average person drank about 8 pints of 'weak beer' a day. It had very little alcohol in it, and even children drank it. It was safer than the water available at the time.

The ending of the marriages of King Henry VIII can be remembered by the following rhyme:
'Divorced, beheaded, died divorced, beheaded, survived'.

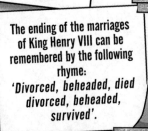

Boudicca
Died between 60 and 62 AD

She was the Queen of the Iceni, an ancient British tribe from East Anglia. When the Romans tried to steal Iceni land and tax the people, Boudicca reportedly raised around 230,000 men to fight against 10,000 Roman soldiers. Somehow the Romans won!

Boudicca, also known as Boudica, Boudiccea or Boudicea, lived nearly 2,000 years ago when Britain was part of the Roman Empire.

The name 'Boudicca' means 'victory'.

Allegedly, when Boudicca realised her army was going to lose the battle, she killed herself by drinking poison, rather than become a Roman prisoner.

A Roman called Dio Cassius described Boudicca as 'tall', 'terrifying', 'fierce', and 'harsh', but also said she was intelligent. He said she had very long, tawny hair and wore a big gold necklace. She also carried a big spear which made her even more scary!

Today, Boudicca, warrior queen of the Iceni, is considered a heroine who stood against the hated Roman invaders. A life-sized statue of her now stands at Westminster Bridge, across from the Houses of Parliament.

Roman Empire

(27 BC – AD 476/1453)

The Romans were responsible for killing many Christians but later they became Christian themselves and the killing stopped.

The Romans came to Britain nearly 2000 years ago (43 AD until 410 AD) and changed our country. Even today, evidence of the Romans being here can be seen in the ruins of Roman buildings, forts, roads and baths found all over Britain.

The Romans were very civilised and their villas had central heating and baths.

Romans loved to make laws, by the end they had written down about 3 million of them. Most of our laws are based on old Roman ones.

In the old Roman calendar there were only 10 months, March was the beginning of the year and there were no months in the winter! The month 'July' is named after the emperor Julius Caesar and 'August' is named after Emperor Augustus.

Pecunia non olet means 'money does not smell'. This phrase was coined as a result of the urine tax charged by the Roman emperors in the 1st century upon the collection of urine. It was used in tanning, and also by launderers as a source of ammonia to clean and whiten woollen togas. There are even isolated reports of it being used as a teeth whitener!

Cleopatra
(69–30 BC)

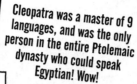

Cleopatra was a master of 9 languages, and was the only person in the entire Ptolemaic dynasty who could speak Egyptian! Wow!

Cleopatra married 2 of her own brothers, ew!

Historians believe that Cleopatra was not stunningly beautiful, but had an ordinary face with a hooked nose, and 'masculine' features.

Cleopatra wasn't Egyptian; she was Greek.

As Queen, Cleopatra was skilled in the arts of warfare. She was a naval commander, and twice led her fleet in battle.

Cleopatra was extremely charismatic and quick-witted. She was very good at persuading people to do things the way she wanted them.

Cleopatra was 39 years old when she died from the bite of a cobra.

Ancient Egypt

(3150 BC – 30 BC)

Ancient Egyptians had great medical skills. They could set broken bones, perform surgeries, and they even developed anaesthetic.

The Ancient Egyptians developed the toilet seat, combs, scissors, make-up, toothpaste and toothbrushes.

Both men and women in Egypt wore make-up to protect their skin from the hot sun.

The Ancient Egyptians measured one hour as one twelfth of the day between sunrise and sunset. This meant that an hour was much longer in summer than in winter.

Pharaoh Pepi II of Egypt used slaves smeared in honey, to attract flies away from him!

The people of Ancient Egypt divided Egypt into two areas. The 'Red Land' was the deserts that protected both sides of Egypt from neighbouring countries and invading armies. The 'Black Land' was the fertile land near the River Nile where people grew their crops.

Nearly all Ancient Egyptian homes had a cat, but cats were not pets. The Ancient Egyptians believed that cats had magical powers. They believed cats protected their homes and children from danger.

Prehistoric Life

(250 million years ago to about 3200BC)

Prehistoric refers to time preceding both human existence and the invention of writing

At one point, all of the Earth's continents are thought to have been connected as one huge land mass. This one huge 'continent' is known as Pangaea.

Archaeology is the study of past human life and culture by the examination of actual evidence, such as graves, buildings, tools and pottery.

Geology is the study of the origin, history, and structure of the Earth.

The Earth is 4.5 billion years old. It took nearly a billion years for the atmosphere to become stable enough to sustain life.

Palaeontology is the study of fossils of life existing in prehistoric times.

To help fight carnivores, many herbivores had natural weapons at their disposal. Examples of this include the spikes on the tail of the stegosaurus and the three horns attached to the front of the triceratops' head.

The largest tooth of any carnivorous dinosaur found to this date is that of a T-rex. It is estimated to have been around 30cm (12in) long including the root.

The Cretaceous era ended with the mass extinction of the dinosaurs. It's widely believed that an asteroid 6 miles in diameter struck the Earth in the Gulf of Mexico, leaving a crater 150 miles wide.

64 million years after dinosaurs became extinct, humans emerged in the Cenozoic era.

Alone

Here I stand side by side
With other evacuated children
On the dusty platform
Waving to my mother, all I want
Is a kiss to say goodbye.
Alone, alone.

Holding a suitcase,
Wearing a gas mask,
Going to an unknown place,
Alone, alone.

I feel like crying
Nobody wants me
My clothes are ragged and dirty.

Children are laughing
Teachers are chattering
But I am
Alone, alone.

It's scary and dark
It's too dark to search for a home
I am tearful and cross
Sitting on the platform
Alone, alone.

Hoping to go back to my precious mother
Waiting on the dusty platform
Longing for some kind person to come
And take me home
But for now, I am
Alone, alone.

Deepti Gautam (10)
Northside Primary School, North Finchley

Dog Fight

Here I stand reading my wife's letter
Saying our house has collapsed
But my six-year-old daughter . . .
Evacuated which made it all better.

Germans are ahead, so I'm going to fight for my country
I hope my daughter has her teddy to remember me even if I'm alive
I hope my wife has said
I love my daughter.

We are preparing for an outbreak
And we will overtake
We have been practising a fake attack
I am scared, so scared that my heart is beating faster than it should.

If I don't survive
I wish to go to Heaven
I love my wife with all my heart
My heart is full of fear
My daughter will have tears trickling down her cheek.

Here I am in the sky in my jet plane
I am in a dog fight
But two more planes come
Boom! I am not dead, luckily I survive
I wonder *where are the Germans?*
I hope my family will still remember me as a brave, strong man
My daughter, I will see her again after a long, cruel war!
I hope she's OK
I want her to get the news that I survived
Meek, meek Mary, the love of my heart.

Sam Izwaini (10)
Northside Primary School, North Finchley

87

Frightened

'London's been bombed', the wireless croaks,
That's what I hear while the fire smokes.
My blood turns cold, my breath filled with frost.
Frightened.

Scared I stand,
My face is bland.
My legs are trembling,
Bold I am not.
Frightened.

Suddenly I think about my son,
In the army, he is one.
Also about my wife,
Who has indeed lost her life.
Frightened.

A crash, a bang, I suddenly hear,
Like someone who is pierced by a spear.
Sadly that is my friend,
Who has known me for many years.
Frightened.

What will I do? I don't know.
Will I be bombed? I don't know.
Shall I mourn someone's death? I don't know.
Who will be dead? I don't know.
Puzzled.
Frightened.

Ricky Luo (10)
Northside Primary School, North Finchley

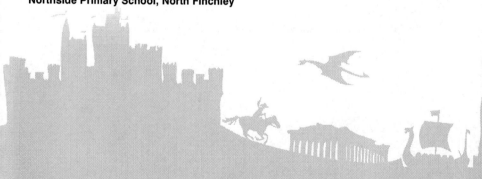

I Don't Know Why

Here I slump in a jolting carriage
I can hear the horses' hooves
Plod, plod, trudge, trudge
On the uneven cobblestones
I'm being sent away to an unknown place
But I don't know why

They give me one thin slice of bread for a meal
I sleep on bitter cold flagstones at night
No one to hug or hold me tight
I am half-starved here
But I don't know why

Fainting all the time from hunger
Permanently light-headed
I went to bed last night
And thought of my beautiful mother
How she hugged me tight
Her soft hair tickling my cheek

I felt my eyes start to close
Heard my breathing slow
Suddenly I stopped thinking
Stopped breathing
Stopped blinking

Dead
But I don't know why.

Jazmine De Grasse (10)
Northside Primary School, North Finchley

Henry VIII's Six Wives

Henry VIII had six wives, six wives And two lost their heads.
I feel sorry for them and I feel their pain.
I see them beheaded,
I hear them screaming
And such a horrible thing to do.
Henry VIII did a horrible thing to his queens.

Amirsadiq Khorsandi-Karimi (8)
Northside Primary School, North Finchley

The Worst Day Of My Life

Here I stand on a cold, cracked platform
Worried, forlorn, down-hearted
Everyone bawling, crying
The train comes right in front of me
I step on the train
I sit down on a cold, dusty seat
I start to cry
My tears falling down my cheek onto my jumper
My mask box got soggy
It took three hours to get to the countryside
I was sick of it
The train stank badly
The train stopped finally
I went next to a house
I was scared to knock
I waited and waited
An old lady stood by the door
She took me in
I went into a room and started crying
I shouted, 'I want to go back home'
Hoping that the war would stop
1st September 1939, I will never get it out of my mind
Or my heart.

Florentina Ramadani (11)
Northside Primary School, North Finchley

The Battle Of Bosworth

I am standing on the battlefield.
I can hear the swords clashing.
I can smell the blood of injured soldiers.
I can hear the calling of both Henry and Richard.
I can feel how Richard and Henry are feeling.
The fear inside me of who's going to win.
Henry or Richard?

Aaliyah Marie Miah (9)
Northside Primary School, North Finchley

Depressed

Here I stand on a dusty platform,
Depressed,
Mum crouching, crying, keeping warm,
Depressed.

The big train comes in a cloud of smoke,
Some children laugh, joke,
But not me, I watch
Depressed.

I wave to Mum,
Depressed,
My throat is numb,
Because I'm so depressed.

I run to the train,
Depressed,
With worries spreading through my brain,
I sit down,
Depressed.

Why is this happening?
I don't want to leave home.
When will this war stop?
I hope it stops soon.

Mishkaat Mamede (10)
Northside Primary School, North Finchley

The Battle Of Bosworth

As the sun rises over the hills,
The horrific battle begins.
The swords clash together with a terrifying clash,
Clink goes the armour as the men begin to fight.

Richard gallops through the crowd,
Swatting and slicing all in his path.
Feeling like a boar who is fighting for his kingdom,
He feels like he could rule the world
With nobody alongside him.

But Henry Tudor has other ideas,
He feels in his heart he's king.
He swots soldiers like flies with the edge of his sword,
Battling for the well-treasured crown.

The fighters trip over the bloody dead,
The arrows hiss past their ears.
Cannonballs bang down on the slippery field,
Who will survive this hell?

Finally, Richard is surrounded,
The boar is now at bay.
Richard is slain, Henry will reign
And the Tudor dynasty begins.

George Hooper-Greenhill (8)
Northside Primary School, North Finchley

Pilot Life

Here I sit flying a plane,
Flying,
Risking my life, at every minute,
Flying,
In the plane every day, every minute,
Flying,
Why? Why me? Why war?

Germans keep bombing, bombing, bombing,
Germans keep bombing every day,
Fighting,
Aircraft guns, shooting at planes,
Fighting,
Sadly, they keep on shooting, shooting, shooting,
Sadly, they keep shooting every single day.

Planes flying around me,
Shooting,
Air raid sirens going off all the time,
Shooting,
Planes exploding and falling out of the sky around me.
Bang! Bang! Bang! Air raid guns shooting,
As petrified as I am, will I die?

Dylan Gondria (10)
Northside Primary School, North Finchley

The Tudor Rhyme

This is my Tudor rhyme,
Try to rhyme it in time,
It's about Henry VIII's life,
And his six wives.
Henry VIII loved tarts,
He also caught Catherine of Aragon's heart,
Henry VIII loved jousting and hunting,
After Catherine came Anne Boleyn.
Henry VIII was posh,
He also had lots of dosh.

Orin Zane-Daley (8)
Northside Primary School, North Finchley

Pilot Life

Here I sit, flying in a plane
Flying
Risking my life, at every minute
Flying
In the plane, every day, every minute
Flying
Why? Why me? Why war?

Germans keep bombing, bombing, bombing
Germans keep bombing every single day
Fighting
Aircraft guns, shooting at planes
Fighting
Sadly, they keep on shooting, shooting, shooting
Sadly, they keep shooting every single day.

Planes flying around me
Shooting
Air raid sirens going off
Shooting
Planes exploding and falling out the sky around me anxiously
Bang! Bang! Bang! Air raid guns shooting
As petrified as I am, will I die?

Anaas Ghalayini (10)
Northside Primary School, North Finchley

The Battle Of Bosworth

Bang, clang, the swords banging and clanging.
Clop, clop, clop, the horse stepping on the ground.
Ting, ting, tang, tang, the shield waving in the air.
Stomp, stomp, people stamping on the field.
Marching, marching, marching, an army marching to the battle.
Fighting . . .
Arrows fly like rockets.
Pikes thrust into the ground.
Scary, many people are dying.
Worried, I worry when this will end.

Sabrina Nazarudin (8)
Northside Primary School, North Finchley

Afraid

Here I stand looking out across the ocean.
Afraid.

Going to defend the French against
The malicious German intruders.
Brave because I have the support of my friends.
Afraid
Because it's my first time in a war.
Afraid.

I hate the Germans
They killed my father
For this reason I went to war.
Afraid.

Now I'm ready to fight
I'm waiting for the Germans.
Afraid.

The Germans are getting there
The fight started.
The Germans bombed the men at the front.
I'm afraid.

Gustavo Fujimoto (10)
Northside Primary School, North Finchley

Evacuation

Here I sit, the train speeding up like a cheetah,
Taking me away from my family.
Here I sit with some of my friends,
But still feeling all alone.
Heading towards the countryside,
Seeing fields and scattered houses.

I'm hearing children screaming and playing,
The train slows down,
I hear children in school,
Playing and having fun.
Maybe everything will be fine?

Ria Shah (10)
Northside Primary School, North Finchley

The Battle Of Bosworth

The Battle of Bosworth started here,
1455, let's be more clear ...
For Richard the third it was not a good year,
Here's what happened, open your ears.

King Edward IV died in vain,
But his 12-year-old son, Edward, was too young to reign.
So his brother, Richard of York, became king
Until Edward grew old enough to rule everything.

Less than a year later, Edward and his bro
Were taken to the Tower of London you know,
By Richard and never seen again,
Presumed dead, nobody knows quite when.

The white rose of York was now in power,
But soon came Henry Tudor's finest hour.
He was from Lancaster, his rose was red,
He wasn't happy and wanted Richard dead.

So the War of the Roses, red and white
Continued, it was a gruesome fight.
The Battle of Bosworth as it was known,
Would see Henry Tudor take over the throne.

Immanuel Isingoma (9)
Northside Primary School, North Finchley

Blood Everywhere

Bloodthirsty, hurting soldiers
Somebody help me!
I'm running out of plasters,
Confused.

The pain is starting everywhere I go,
People screaming,
Asking for help,
'Nurse, nurse! Help us!'

Everyone asking for help,
Oh no!
I feel like I'm alone,
Why is this happening to us?
Did I do something wrong?

I hope my family are still alive,
Imagine all the people,
Nothing to kill or die for,
Only people, no war!
Boom!

Stop Hitler! Turn off the radio,
Guns shooting, *pow!*

Renée Grace Manalo (10)
Northside Primary School, North Finchley

Why?

Here I stand looking, wondering
Why he's bleeding?
Why this is happening?
Why my husband left me here all alone?

The terror rushing up to me
The sadness catching me
When will my man come back?
When will I get my life back?

Why can't the Germans say sorry?
Why can't they just make this all end?
They took my husband away
Without a blink of an eye.

Why did the Germans come here of all places?
Why did they choose my home?
It's made me angry, it's mad me sad
I don't know how to feel anymore
I don't care anymore
I just want to die.

Sandra Madubuike (10)
Northside Primary School, North Finchley

Bomb Disposal

Here I stand in a muddy French field
As I am cutting wires,
With my tatty shirt,
This is my job.
My job is to stop bombs from exploding.
As me and my friend dig a hole and find a bomb,
As my friend said, 'I will do it.'
'Why?'
'Because I need to do it.'
'Why?'
'Just stop saying why and step away.'
As the bomb exploded
And my friend died.

Deniss Mirt (10)
Northside Primary School, North Finchley

Crash!

Here I stand
Terrified of the bomb falling down
Crash!
I ran to the shelter to be
Safe and warm.
I felt the terror inside my body
I felt the cold going through my body.
Crash!
The bombs fell down.

I came out slowly from the shelter
And saw my house crashed down
On the floor in pieces.
I started to cry for a while
But then I stopped and thought about
My life.
What will I do with myself?
Crash!
A bomb fell down
But now I didn't care
I just wanted to die.

Sandra Szczepanek (10)
Northside Primary School, North Finchley

Frightened

Here I stand on the front line, getting ready to fight France.
Frightened.
Going to defend France from Germany.
Malicious Germans.
Frightened.
Brave to fight Germany and to defend France.
Frightened.
My bullets finished
Don't know what to do.
Frightened.
Running for my life, I don't want to die.
Frightened.
My house has been bombed.
My mother and my brothers and sisters homeless
Don't know what to do.
Frightened.
German planes over Britain, fighting for our lives.
Frightened.

Isaac Abdulahi (10)
Northside Primary School, North Finchley

In A Land Girl's Life

In a land girl's life there is lots to do
Milking mooing cows
Producing fresh milk
Hearing the cockerel crow
Hens with feathers like silk
Oval-shaped eggs off-white and brown
Saddling the white ponies
Driving the filthy yellow tractor
This life is exciting

Apple trees as green as grass
Apple pie and apple tarts
The freshly ploughed yard
The comforting feel of long, emerald grass.

Salma Mouradi (10)
Northside Primary School, North Finchley

King Henry VIII And Six Wives

King Henry ate pies
And married six times.

First wife, Catherine of Aragon divorced
And second wife Anne Boleyn beheaded.

Third wife, Jane Seymour died
And fourth wife, Anne of Cleves divorced.

Fifth wife, Katherine Howard beheaded
And final wife, Catherine Parr survived.

Catherine of Aragon's daughter was Mary
Married King Phillip of Spain.

Queen Elizabeth didn't get married
Or have any children.

King Edward VI didn't marry
Or have any children either.

Prisha Dubey (9)
Northside Primary School, North Finchley

Help!

German planes are coming
Help!
I'm scared
I, a pilot in the British Air Force.
Help!
What will happen?
Only God knows.
Boom!

The pain is relying on the soul of the wings
The pain is relying on the soul of the guns
The pain is relying on the soul of me
Me
A pilot
A pilot in the Royal Air Force.
Help!

Sumit Sethi (10)
Northside Primary School, North Finchley

In The Hospital

Here I stand in the hospital
Putting bandages in people's bodies
Helping them to be healed.

I can hear people screaming,
I can see people injured
And I can smell the dust of the bombs.
Soldiers broken by the war.

Frightened of the German bombers
And worried about my family.
Hoping that no one will die
And my family will be safe.

All nurses working for their families
All working hard and all scared.
I am a nurse.
When will this war end?

Mary Lorraine Israel (10)
Northside Primary School, North Finchley

What Am I To Do?

Here I stand, my home is crushed,
Windows are smashed, dust scattered everywhere.

In London a city destroyed,
What am I to do?
My family are dead.

Where am I to go?
Frightened and sad, all alone.
What am I to do?

Searching through the rubble,
Looking for my precious possessions.
A broken lamp, a ripped book,
A smashed photo of my father.

What am I to do?

Puria Tavakol (10)
Northside Primary School, North Finchley

Sadness

Here I am standing on the platform
Some children are crying, some are laughing
But all are sad inside.
Sadness.

The thought of missing my family
I am upset and depressed
Tears dropping down my cheek
The train is puffing away
While everyone is crying.
Sadness.

I am praying for the war to end.
Sadness.

Nikolay Iliev (10)
Northside Primary School, North Finchley

The Greeks' Freedom

T he Greeks were battling their enemies.
H orses were charging at the soldiers.
E normous horses were running towards the warriors.

G uarding soldiers fighting their enemies.
R aging men dying and killing.
E normous horses jumping about.
E ager soldiers ready to fight.
K illing opposition, Greeks won.
S hield blocking the enemy.

F ighting Greeks winning the war.
R aging horses kicking their enemy.
E ager soldiers winning the war.
E ager soldiers won the war.
D angerous weapons flying through the air.
O pposite sides fighting back.
M ad soldiers fighting back.

Rodgers Brave Omondi (8)
Purwell Primary School, Hitchin

Queen Boudicca

Today we are going back in time,
To do some Celt and Roman rhyme.
Queen Boudicca I recommend,
She will not have been a very nice friend.
She was not very kind, if that's what you had in mind.
The queen harmed many Romans since she was not very keen on them,
She started attacking at 5am.
She killed many Romans in her path,
So don't mess with her wrath
Or you will be chopped in half.
I promise I won't lie,
If you mess with her you will die!
Bang! Wallop!
You're Roman pie!
She is very brave and bold,
This would knock you out cold,
I warn you when you are told.
She would hurt Romans, rain or frost no matter what the cost.
But one day the deed was done,
And Queen Boudicca drank poison and was gone . . .
Therefore . . .
Goodbye Queen Boudicca big and strong, Roman serial killer!

Oliver Barker (8)
Purwell Primary School, Hitchin

The War Of Rome Poem

People fighting with swords in front of me.
I can see soldiers falling to the ground.
I can see golden shields thrashing together.
Silver swords crashing together with might.
Splintering wooden shields touching my skin.
Silver swords cutting me.
Shields hitting my tummy, very painful indeed.
I can smell revolting blood on the ground.
I can smell the sweat dripping off my head.
The fresh smell of Roman sword is up my nose.

Dillon Dimmock (9)
Purwell Primary School, Hitchin

The Powerful Queen

She lived with a king.
Her husband shared the city.
Boudicca was queen

'Leave our place alone!'
In the kingdom Romans stole.
Vanish the army.
Determined army.
Our team is greater than the Celts.
Our soldiers are strong.

War is what we want.
It was a gruesome battle.
Terrifying Rome.
Her husband was smart.

Her daughters were powerful.
Ever so bold queen.
Rotten Romans are violent.

Kicking so madly
It was such a great battle.
Nearly best as war.
Get down here at once.

Millie Stearn (8)
Purwell Primary School, Hitchin

The Greeks

T he arrow shooting away to the opponent.
H orses jumping at the rivals.
E nemies trying to kill the good people.

G reeks angrily fighting.
R ough fighting men begin to work hard.
E xcitingly the horses jump.
E vil men sneak towards the Greeks.
K nights charging into battle.
S pears zoom through the air.

Sami Malik (7)
Purwell Primary School, Hitchin

The Greeks' Battles

T he fighting Greeks.
H urrying enemies going to kill.
E nemies losing men.

G reek people.
R eeking enemies.
E nemies lost the battle.
E nemies killing Greeks.
K illing Greeks.
S tanding tall bald tree.

B ig huge battle.
A ncient battle.
T errible battle.
T errified soldiers.
L ying enemies.
E vil enemies.
S ome brave Greeks.

Gabriel McFall (8)
Purwell Primary School, Hitchin

The Greek Charge

T he soldiers are brave to fight in fierce battles.
H orses gallop wildly towards the enemies.
E nemies charge to the other group fighting on its way.

G reat shining swords wave curiously.
R ound hard shining shields shine brightly in the sun's glow.
E ven though there are fierce horses they miss.
E legant chariots around the horses.
K illing villains are willing to kill.

C runching flags gently sway in the breeze.
H urrying and dashing to their villains.
A ny soldier is brave to fight.
R aging soldiers charge anywhere near enemies.
G reek soldiers are dying to fight.
E legant, shining glow in the sun's bright glow.

Sanjeeda Alam (8)
Purwell Primary School, Hitchin

She Was Boudicca

S he lived with a king.
H er daughters were powerful.
E ver so brave queen.

W ar is our name.
A rea we conquer.
S he is strong.

B lood does pour.
O rder more men now.
U nhappy war.
D ead bodies.
I t was a gruesome battle.
C uts came like flies.
C elts fled like horses.
A ll the Celts were heartbroken.

Oscar Earle (8)
Purwell Primary School, Hitchin

The Greek Battle

T he Greeks fighting for freedom
H eads chopped off
E nemies dying.

G reeks praying to God not to die
R aging army
E very Greek killed is an enemy
E very person died
K aboom goes the whips through the air.

B ig chariots break the doors open
A ctually the Greeks won the battle.
T he horses charging for freedom.
T he Greeks slaughtering
L ions spears pointing
E nemies kill Greeks.

Fletcher Millar (7)
Purwell Primary School, Hitchin

107

The Greeks

F ierce, frightened Greeks sprinting into battle
I ron starting to get hot on the bottom of the horses feet
G uns shooting wildly everywhere
H orses charging into battle
T errified horses trembling, trying not to get hit
I mmediately a spear came flying over the sky
N arrow swords dropped onto the floor
G unpowder exploding everywhere

G alloping horses
R acing horses clash into each other
E ars listening for enemies
E ighty people fighting for freedom
K eeping horses safe and covered
S addles coming loose.

Lucy King (7)
Purwell Primary School, Hitchin

The Greeks

F ighting so hard
I gnorant enemies struggling for cover
G olden spears flying through the air
H ot people just getting hotter
T he soldiers shout, 'Fall back!'
I ron chariots
N aughty enemies shout hooray
G hosts haunt the battlefield

G reeks rule
R unning for freedom
E normous whips smacking the air
E very soldier is nearly killed
K nights fighting as well
S laying their enemies.

Vaughn Doggett (7)
Purwell Primary School, Hitchin

Fighting Greeks

F inding their way through the crowd.
I gnoring the enemies and defeating them.
G oing for the enemies.
H iding from the nasty ones.
T ired, wanting to go home they still do it.
I n the night wanting to win they know they can do it.
N ow they get their own back.
G etting more and more tired.

G alloping horses in the sunlight.
R acing to win the battle.
E ach of them did great.
E xcellent battle.
K indly the boss gave the other team a prize.

Lauren Taylor (8)
Purwell Primary School, Hitchin

Roman War

Sniffing the rotten blood,
Boudicca dragged her boots through the thick Roman mud.

Clasping the heavy splintered oak spear,
Boudicca charged with no fear.

Listening to the Roman shrieks of fear,
Boudicca gave a proud loud cheer.

Gazing as the Roman bodies fall,
Boudicca didn't care at all.

Worrying villagers scampered away,
But Boudicca was determined to stay.

Ella Lewis (8)
Purwell Primary School, Hitchin

Greek Battle

G reat battling everywhere.
R oaring Greeks to scare the baddies.
E nemies fighting to win.
E normous whips whacking the horses to make them go faster.
K wishing whips making the noise kwish.

B attling Greeks and horses.
A rmour shining in the sun.
T rees with chopped off leaves and whirly branches.
T he great Greeks
L ong spears in the soldiers hands.
E verybody is battling.

Mollie Jervis (7)
Purwell Primary School, Hitchin

The Greeks

T he battling Greeks fight against the other side.
H uge spears come down from the sky.
E nemies dodging the other side.

G etting tired.
R aging enemies.
E nemies' clothes are camouflaged.
E xplosions all over are used with bombs.
K eeping calm.
S oldiers charging to the enemy.

Meth Wijeyekoon (7)
Purwell Primary School, Hitchin

The Roman And Celtic War Poem

Determined, I hold my silver sword trying to look fierce.
Frightened and scared I lift my shield with blood dripping down it.
Gazing, I look across to the river seeing it going up and down.
Terrified I stare at Boudicca, was she going to kill me?
Shivering I stare at the angry Romans wondering if I should surrender.

Stacey Abbiss (8)
Purwell Primary School, Hitchin

Fighting With The Celts

Boudicca was persevering in war.
She tried to be very unbeatable.
However she was very tough in battle.
She is charging to be very brave too.
Marching she could hear sharp howls of pain.
Soon she could smell revolting bodies.
Terrified, the Celts fought the brave Romans.
Soon the Celts were determined to come first.

Nicola Carr (8)
Purwell Primary School, Hitchin

The Battle

I can see dead people on the pavement
I can see Celts dying in the battle
I can feel the golden sword in my hand
I can feel the sweat dropping down my face
I can hear the Roman army shouting
I can hear the Celts screaming with pain
I can smell blood flowing across the pavement
I can smell the death of the army.

Michael Brookes (8)
Purwell Primary School, Hitchin

Powerful Boudicca

Trying to dodge the unbeatable Celtic soldiers struggling through them.
With all their strength to beat the unbeatable Boudicca.
Clashing their silver swords against the Celts.
I can smell the revolting scent of the rotten Romans.
Leaping with all their might, the Roman soldiers glide with their swords and shields.

Maisie Jayne Brett (8)
Purwell Primary School, Hitchin

The Wartime

Scared soldiers fighting for their lives
Planes over my head, dropping bombs
People running for their lives
Guns being fired all around
Bombs lighting up the sky
Too bright to look
Soldiers losing their lives

People fighting each other
People getting diseases and dying
Everyone is alarmed
People lying there with bullet holes in them
The place is dark and gloomy
Thunder roaring around us
People getting tortured around me

I'm so frightened
I'm getting threatened by people
I'm very badly wounded
I can't stand it
I've got a disease
I'm nearly dying

Please somebody help me!

Megan Bonney (9)
St Joseph's Catholic Primary School, Bishop's Stortford

War

War is a terrifying place.
It's the last place on Earth that I want to be in.
I can feel the squelching mud beneath my feet.
My friends dying right before my eyes.

I never wanted to be here in the first place.
All the soldiers are starving or terribly ill.
I can't bear it.
I hate it here!

But I know we will win.

Annabelle McKelvey (9)
St Joseph's Catholic Primary School, Bishop's Stortford

Revenge

I worked in a map shop which was very old.
It was pouring down with rain.
Suddenly there was a scream, Blackbeard killed my family!

He had a sword which was glistening like the sun.
It made me look away.
He caught me watching, so he pulled out his poison dart.
I am on his ship.

I woke up.
Blackbeard put me up against the wall.
Tell me where the treasure is!
Draw me a map!
After six hours I finished the map.
Blackbeard snatched it off me.

At midnight I went to a lifeboat.
I escaped and ran for my life to get to shore.
The Spanish army helped me kill Blackbeard.
I saw the ship.
I said fire all you have.
People were firing guns and cannons.
His ship was sinking.
Was that the end of Blackbeard?

Rhys Haupt (9)
St Joseph's Catholic Primary School, Bishop's Stortford

The War

The war is terrifying.
The war is as scary place.
The war is freezing.
The war is really, really sad.
The Germans are coming.
The guns are shooting.
Guns, guns, guns, guns, guns, guns
Bang!

Jack Revell (9)
St Joseph's Catholic Primary School, Bishop's Stortford

The Ancestors

You know those ape people,
They were the cavemen.
Their names were the ancestors,
They smelt like raw flesh.
They looked like cheeky chimps, but mark
My words, they were not wimps.

They were as hairy as a monkey
And they were really tough.
All you could hear were grunts,
But they made me flinch.
Plus you wouldn't like them in a strap.

When they hunt they killed.
They never needed a pill.
Warthog spotted, lie low.
Death to the hog! Woah!
Now it had eaten, yum!
It was nice in its tum.

It's dark,
Time to rest.
It was silent, scary too.
It's not strange.

Noel O'Loughlin (9)
St Joseph's Catholic Primary School, Bishop's Stortford

Olympus And The Underworld

Some people wonder why winter comes, well it all started in Ancient Greece.
When young Persephone was kidnapped by Hades,
God of the Underworld.
Demeter the mother of Persephone grew angry and angrier and she let no crops grow.
So Hades let Persephone go with her mother, but only half of the year.
And that is why winter comes.

Alejandra Hooker Niembro (9)
St Joseph's Catholic Primary School, Bishop's Stortford

114

Diary Of The First World War

The soldiers fight away
And the planes fly up high.
I can feel the cold wind
And see a different soldier die.

The guns fire away
And cannonballs shooting out.
I can see one of my friends die
And the crowd cheer and shout.

I hear the swords and cannonballs as
The army start to fight.
Rain comes pouring down and there is
No light.

I feel alarmed.
The air is as cold as ice.
It looks horrible
And so vile.

I can't live any longer.
I can remember what I said . . .
Believe in myself.
But now . . . I am dead!

Charlie Gatward (9)
St Joseph's Catholic Primary School, Bishop's Stortford

Olympus Hercules

I am lost in a kind of maze.
My eyes are lost in a kind of gaze.
Bubbling and boiling green liquid.
His head is filled with rage,
Almost as hot as the green liquid.
Hades is glowing with fire.
Souls hearts filled with rage.

Hades' heart is burning with ferociousness as hot as the sun.
He's got my friend, I'm going to get him back.
I feel sick and dizzy as if I am being hypnotised.

Ali Butt (9)
St Joseph's Catholic Primary School, Bishop's Stortford

Queen Goes Past

There she was going past.
Looking very proud.
She had a beautiful golden crown.
With a lovely silky gown.

I really was jolly glad.
It was an opportunity.
I was walking through the crowd.
Could I get a closer view?

Shall I tell you who she was?
Oh yes I will because . . .
She was Cleopatra the queen.
Do you know where I was?

She was on a lovely boat.
On the river Nile.
It was particularly hot.
No rain or cloud just a red-hot sun.

Cleopatra was so beautiful.
My dad's eyes popped out of his head.
My mum said, 'It's time to go,' I said a vast no.
But that was the end of my fun, you should try to see her one day.

Francesca Luppi (9)
St Joseph's Catholic Primary School, Bishop's Stortford

Cavaliers Vs Roundheads!

It was 1603, the English Civil War.
King Charles the Ist vs Oliver Cromwell.
There was blood and guts everywhere.
Both armies started to get terrified.
Charles could see the enemies approaching.
Oliver wanted to kill Charles, Charles wanted to kill Oliver.

I'm on the Cavalier's side and I can see death everywhere.
It's so deadly, I can't watch anymore.
It's all glory, the battle started an hour ago.
I'm going to be killed any second now . . .

Ailsa Kenny (9)
St Joseph's Catholic Primary School, Bishop's Stortford

Vikings Of War

Vikings are rough.
Vikings are tough.
But they're much worse than that.
They have a sword,
That won't make you bored.
They will make you terrified.
They will kill you if you run.
Bombs bang and crash.
They have an axe,
That you will not be able to lift.
You can hear the bangs from the catapults.
Nobody is safe.
You can smell the smoke from the fire and now you see,
They are much worse than me.
Sweat will run down your face.
You know that this is a horrible place.
But they do not know.
Well, you already know,
That they are fighting to the death!

Rhiannon Conway (8)
St Joseph's Catholic Primary School, Bishop's Stortford

The King And The Wife

It was one horrible morning when I heard the news.
My mistress said she may have to die.
So I went to the cruel king begging for mercy.
Suddenly they said no to my request.
I done my chores but I didn't mind.

The next day I got the Queen's best dress, she went to her trial.
I did my chores really well because it would be the last thing I do for her.

She came back from her trial.
She got a letter, she asked me to read it.
She was found guilty as I left, bursting into tears.
It was a horrible day, it was the day of the execution.
It was disgusting, yuck. I was heartbroken and horrified and fuming.

Elodie Gibby (9)
St Joseph's Catholic Primary School, Bishop's Stortford

Die-No Time!

Once there were dinosaurs in the world.
There were plant and meat-eaters.
They had to charge at each other.
There was a lot of blood.
Others just ran away.
It was really sad to see.

But that was not the end.
So when a meat-eater awoke.
Plant-eaters were really scared.
Some tried to run away.
But they were eaten.
They started roaring because they were scared.

Millions of years past.
Dinosaurs are extinct.
It is a gloomy, deadly place.
Nobody is living now.
So I went away.

Mateusz Zawadzki (8)
St Joseph's Catholic Primary School, Bishop's Stortford

Dinosaurs

I am a bug living in the forest.
I'm black and not very big.
Rustling of the trees and squelching of the mud.
There is something coming for me, I better run.
Oh gosh, oh no, it's a dinosaur.
Tremendous stomping, it's getting louder.

It's running, it has spotted me.
I'm going to be his lunch!
It's getting closer and closer.
How am I going to survive?
It has got hold of me.
It's putting me in its mouth.
He does not chew he just swallows.
I wish I was not hurt.

Antonella Amorelli (9)
St Joseph's Catholic Primary School, Bishop's Stortford

Work, Terrible Work!

We Victorian children are forced to do horrible jobs.
We have to polish all the black leading.
The people we work for are obnoxious and mean.
They make us climb up chimneys, it's really hard.

If we get hurt we will just be replaced.
We hardly get paid anything at all.
It is totally unfair.
Still there is nothing we can do, we have no power.

Our mothers and fathers pretend we are six.
Really we are only four.
They send us to so we can get money for the family.
We are very sad they do this.

Everyone, all the children who do these jobs,
All have one dream, that's all and it is . . .
School, school is what we want.
We want an education.

Emilia Boylan (8)
St Joseph's Catholic Primary School, Bishop's Stortford

The Day I Went To A Gladiator Match

I went to a match and I brought my book.
The reason I bought it 'cause I didn't want to look.
A man took my book and he wouldn't give it back.
So I said in my head, 'What a lack!'
'Oooh, aaah,' I didn't want to look!
Ooh, he had a hook!
I wished I could eat a Nic-Nac or get my book back.
It was not very pleasant,
Trust me, it was very unpleasant.
It was a lot of mess,
And not very religious.
'Ooooow! He is killed!'
He should have used his shield.
Then the man gave me back my book which was so formal.
I was glad everything was back to normal.

Eve Rooney (9)
St Joseph's Catholic Primary School, Bishop's Stortford

119

I Wish I Never Came To War

I feel cold.
I wish I never came to war.
I am frightened.
The noise around me is horrible, I wish I never heard it.

I am wounded.
I wish I never came to war.
I am really tired.
The trenches are flooding so there is nowhere to stay.

Bombs are blowing up.
I wish I never came to war.
My ears are about to pop.
The enemies are approaching me now it is my turn to fight.

Guns are firing.
I wish I never to war.
Planes above me are trying to shoot me.
I wish I never came to war.

Isabella Silvester (9)
St Joseph's Catholic Primary School, Bishop's Stortford

The Trenches

I'm stuck in these trenches throwing grenades and fighting.
I don't know how much longer I can stand this.
I can't stand thinking how long I'm going to be here.
Weeks, months, maybe years.
I'm scared, terrified and furious to hear the shrieks of bombing and death.

I'm alarmed when I see dead bodies on the ground.
I think the Germans have taken over the country.
I can hear the stomping and approaching of the Germans.
Guns are firing, mud is being squelched, bombs are exploding
and bullets are striking!

But we're not giving up, even if they're intimidating us.
I'm here to fight for my country, I'm never going to give up.
The Germans are really powerful and I'm fighting for my life being the best
soldier there has ever been.

Lorenzo Fabrizi
St Joseph's Catholic Primary School, Bishop's Stortford

Survive

Blood is running down my face.
Bullets are flying over me.
People are lying on the ground.
Rain is pouring over me.
Bombs are exploding.
Lightning is striking.
Thunder is booming.
Flames are blazing.
My clothes are wrecked.
People are crying for help.
Germans are terrorizing.
Planes are flying.
I'm running down the trenches.
People are frightened.
My friends are dying.
Death is coming.

Sean King (9)
St Joseph's Catholic Primary School, Bishop's Stortford

Soldiers Fighting

It was a rainy and stormy day.
All the soldiers were getting prepared.
Then it all started.

Sitting on my window sill.
Waiting for all of it to start.

It started, I saw bombs going off.
I felt frightened, terrorised and scared.
I heard marching outside.
I saw shadows and furious people.

It was night-time, we had to go to sleep.
It was still going on. I could not get to sleep.
I just wanted all of this to stop!
I wish all of this would stop!

Devon Keane-Goldhawk (9)
St Joseph's Catholic Primary School, Bishop's Stortford

121

Deadly War

The roar of crashing planes.
The thrashing of the fight.
The ticking of the bombs.
Boom! One of the bombs exploded.

The screaming of the soldiers.
The violence of the war.
The deadliness of the guns.
Boom! One more dead.

The diabolical pain.
The unpleasant smell.
The unsafe battlefield.
Boom! I'm dead . . .

Emily Jackson (9)
St Joseph's Catholic Primary School, Bishop's Stortford

Death Surrounds

Death surrounds the day on the 5th of May.
Gladiators come out to stay,
Fighting.
Dying.
Escape the torture.
Madness!

Sword vs sword.
Who's going to win?
Stab!
Jab!
One of the gladiators is on the floor.
'Die!' called one of the gladiators.

Paul Wood (9)
St Joseph's Catholic Primary School, Bishop's Stortford

A Girl Who Lived

'The time has come for your head to come off.'
I was broken-hearted, tears dropping from my face.
They walked to the front of the garden
There was the gallows.
I was scared, I didn't know what to do.

But really I was terrorised.
What was happening?
I hadn't done anything wrong.
I didn't want to die because I loved him.
I didn't understand why this was happening to me.
But I was washing the floor all night and all day, in the morning and all.
So why would I be here if I did all the cleaning?

Isa-Bella Brooks (9)
St Joseph's Catholic Primary School, Bishop's Stortford

Vile Victorians

I am working in a country house with tears running down my face.
I am tired and boiling with nothing to drink.
I don't think I have any saliva in my mouth,
Three days without water, next day four.
We only get a drink once a day sometimes not at all.
I have to clean the bedrooms and clean all the leaves out of the pool.
Tidy up the kitchen, also the bathroom.
Our cruel landowner is mean and horrible.
I am terrorised by her, no shoes to wear.
Old clothes torn and almost coming off.
I wish I was a normal child, my feet are
Bleeding and I want to run away.

Jolie Difrancesco (9)
St Joseph's Catholic Primary School, Bishop's Stortford

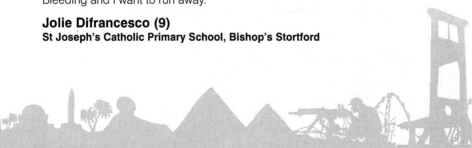

Bad Feelings In World War II

A tear rolled down my cheek when I heard Hitler speak.
He had an evil glint in his eye.
I knew a lot of people would die.
With bombs, men and planes, he attacked again and again.

It was so normal in life.
Happy, cheerful.
But now all is changed,
When suddenly bombs would arrive again.
With bombs, men and planes, he attacked again and again.
I wished it had not happened.
I was done for and would not survive.

Yazmin Layzell (9)
St Joseph's Catholic Primary School, Bishop's Stortford

I Came To War

I came to war.
I hate it, blood is everywhere.
Bullets are roaring like a bear.
Pistols are firing into the head.
Push on the trigger, out comes the bullet.
Into the head of my friend.
Tommy guns are firing.
My friends are dying.
And the world is puffing smoke.
Terrorists are killing and warriors
Puffing and people drop with tears.

Luca Lewis (9)
St Joseph's Catholic Primary School, Bishop's Stortford

Cleopatra's Plan

I was in ancient Egypt when Cleopatra was alone.
She said that she could kill her husband tonight when he was asleep in bed.

She said to herself I hate that husband.
Behind his back what she did say, 'He was lazy, husband of mine.'
She moaned this all to her husband.
He heard everything behind the door.

He thought, to get this out of her mind
The husband was going to run away.
He was going to run away to central
Africa as soon as he saw a . . .

Madeleine Blackburn (9)
St Joseph's Catholic Primary School, Bishop's Stortford

Me In War

I can feel the wind going across my face and I feel the coldness of the air.
I see grenades being thrown.
I feel the blaze of fire and the fizzing of the fire.
I hear machine guns drilling and bombers scraping and whistling.
Soldiers frightened of dying.
Then I hear grenades exploding.

Martin Tran (9)
St Joseph's Catholic Primary School, Bishop's Stortford

Head Banging World War II

Banging in my head. It goes *Boom! Boom!*
Hitler's voice in every room.
The house next door was just blown up.
I'm holding on to my helpless mum.
I have to go down to the cellar,
Where I shout Hitler is a nasty fellow.

Olivia Dodd (9)
St Joseph's Catholic Primary School, Bishop's Stortford

War

I see the planes slicing through the sky.
Like eagles hunting for their prey.
I hear the machine guns firing like marching bands.
Consistently stomping on the ground.

I feel proud of myself for not giving up, through bucketing rain.
But sometimes I just want to drag my bones across the battlefield back home.

Bullets are firing, men are dying,
I am crying to go back home.
The war is still going on, when will it stop?
All I know is that soon I will drop.

Matthew Ryan (8)
St Joseph's Catholic Primary School, Bishop's Stortford

Captain Pink Pants

The scallywags that stay on my stupid ship!
The grub on the floor that my
Slaves should surely clean!
The gold on the floor, oh pick it up already
The poo on the floor that belongs
To my dog Freddy
The noise of the seagulls, how I want to
Hit them hard and
Horribly!
The frying in the galley
Fizz, fizz all day, it's
Annoying!
Oh and I feel so angry
As much as er . . . er, well an angry thing.

James Loughrey (7)
St Margaret Clitherow RC Primary School, Stevenage

9/11

One sunny morning,
In the city of NY,
People in the shower,
Getting out of bed.
But . . .
A jet plane has been hijacked,
They don't know where it's going
It's heading straight for NY!
My dad is on that flight line, will he be OK?
Everyone is worried,
Especially me!
And of course my dad!
OMG, what's happening?
It flew into the tower,
The sirens of the cops,
And the fire crew.
People jump out the window,
Paperwork is flying.
And lots of metal steel.
This is serious.
They're sending out the choppers,
To find out what to do,
They have realised what has happened.
Another plane has hit the other tower.
Over 2,000 people dead,
My dad is OK.
God bless America!

Josh Curtis (9)
St Margaret Clitherow RC Primary School, Stevenage

My War

M en risking their lives for Britain
Y ou are now safe because war is ending

W atch the sky and beware!
A ware of the planes in the sky they might drop bombs
R emember the war!

Jada Green (10)
St Margaret Clitherow RC Primary School, Stevenage

World War II From A Child's Eyes

I can see . . .
The light of booming, crashing bombs and crawling fire
The blood around me is German blood
I can't stand it, stand it,
But I can a bit
I can's see why mum is taking me to the station
I wish I could hold my concentration.

I can hear . . .
I can hear people screaming and breathing hoping the War would stop
The noise is terrible
I nearly cry when I go to the train station
But I don't understand
I don't like the train station or the train
I cry as I am in some station
I feel sick but never am
But I feel the pain.

I can feel . . .
The sadness around the place
I'd rather die but I can't do it
The kids at the school laugh
It seems I need to run out of the way.

Ella Hicks (8)
St Margaret Clitherow RC Primary School, Stevenage

My Pirate's Secret Poem

Flags are flapping crazy like a hummingbird's wing.
Boats and ships crashing badly to beaches and shores.
Bottles with paper inside crashing to shore.
Pirates falling off ships with their clothes all torn.

I hear big waves crashing to rocks and beaches.
I hear pirates stealing ships and buried treasure chests.

I smell delicious bacon and yummy boiled eggs.
I smell the salty seawater falling on the ship.

I feel salty water falling on my toes and it itches so badly.

Bethany da Rocha (7)
St Margaret Clitherow RC Primary School, Stevenage

World War II From A Child's Eyes

I can see . . .
Enormous bombs shooting down.
My mum with a frown deciding for me to be evacuated with different people to different places.
My suitcase ready to pack, a pile of clothes and a snack.
People at the station with their mothers but no dads.
Everyone wearing neat brown tags!

I can hear . . .
The children wailing, screaming, crying.
Mothers with teary eyes as we wave our final goodbyes.
Everyone crying on the way there, people trying not to stare.
Children chatting, all calmed down while I was listening to the train's clinking and clanking sound.
Now we've reached the countryside I can hear the birds singing lovely songs
And huge white things with black spots making an odd mooing noise.

I can feel . . .
My heart pounding and racing trying to see who's going to pick me.
Lonely and frightened and thinking someone choose me.
Here comes a couple with smiling faces.
I put on a cute voice.
They say, 'We'll take him!'

Holly King (8)
St Margaret Clitherow RC Primary School, Stevenage

The War

People fighting in the war,
Some are bombing my front door.
The best soldier has a cool gun,
I can't believe it, the war is done.
If you get hurt you can technically die,
But if it's bad, people will cry.
I know the army is a bit too violent,
I don't know how soldiers get their army licence,
When on Earth will this war end?
Shells, bullets, bombs and grenades, they all seem to blend.

Giordano Di Credico (10)
St Margaret Clitherow RC Primary School, Stevenage

129

Pirate Ship

See?
I see the flag waving like paper
I see a cannonball firing towards us
I see the buried treasure
I see the cannon ready to fire

Hear?
I hear the cannonball booming
I hear the sword clanging
I hear the gun banging
I hear the pirates shouting

Smell?
I smell the sea
I smell the bacon
I smell the pollution
I smell the poison

Feel?
I feel really brave
I feel really tough and strong
I feel really seasick
I feel really like I'm going to vomit.

Rigel Thaddeus Maclyn Pagcu (7)
St Margaret Clitherow RC Primary School, Stevenage

Environment

E vironment is a part of the world we live in
N ever stop caring about how we live in it
V ery special care needs to be taken
I n what we do
R esponsibility is individual
O f course sometimes we have to remind each other
N ow
M oney can be made from recycled goods
E nergy can be made and produced from recycled goods
N ow is the time to do your bit
T oday, start thinking about your environment.

Chloe McDonald (10)
St Margaret Clitherow RC Primary School, Stevenage

The Dinosaurs

I've travelled back in time,
To the dinosaurs,
I hear a roar from a dinosaur,
It's tall,
It's ferocious,
It's a T-rex,

It's hard to run away,
Keep down, stay still,
It's gone away,
Down below I feel mud,
I look down,
It's animal dung,

I want to go home,
But it's not time to leave,
Just look at this,
It's a jungle in here,
Oh no, where am I?
Oh good I'm out,
I'm back home,
For now!

Natasha Thompson (10)
St Margaret Clitherow RC Primary School, Stevenage

A Secret Pirate Ship

In the beginning there was nothing
But now there's something
A Jolly Roger pirate ship waving
Its flag wildly like a kite.

You can hear the flag waving in the moonlight.
When the men are snoring you can hear the flag roaring.

You can smell the sea
When the pirates are drinking tea.

You can feel the flag
Waving like a fan in the sky.

Lola Tobin (7)
St Margaret Clitherow RC Primary School, Stevenage

A Dinosaur's Planet

Dinosaurs are extinct,
And birds like ostriches are linked.
Don't worry if the dinosaurs come back,
Just give them a whack.
Saurpods are herbivores,
And in the dinosaur time there weren't any laws.
We still have dinosaurs on our planet,
If I could name a female dinosaur,
I would call it dangerous Janet.
Pterodactyls are dinosaurs that fly,
If I saw a T-rex I wouldn't dare say hi.
Some dinosaurs are tall,
And some dinosaurs are small.
Some dinosaurs have features,
And if I made up dinosaur food,
I would call it queathers.
Some people say dinosaurs roar,
Some people think dinosaurs have claws.
Some dinosaurs are alright,
Some dinosaurs are quite light.

Maiya Stevens-Howe (10)
St Margaret Clitherow RC Primary School, Stevenage

Greek Monsters

Dangerous, scary, fierce creatures,
All with phenomenal features!
Roaring loudly, flying high,
Breathing fire to the sky!
Medusa's hair is made of snakes,
Her eyes, some small snowflakes!
Minotaur eats everyone,
Which you will find is so not fun!
Harpies steal all my food,
And that puts me in a horrid mood!
Dangerous, scary, fierce creatures,
All with phenomenal features.

Grace Tobias (9)
St Margaret Clitherow RC Primary School, Stevenage

World War II From A Child's Eyes

I can see . . .
Massive bombs swooping from above
Enemy tanks, terrifying our mothers
Sobbing all around
London on fire, fighting for justice
Brothers and sisters saying, 'Farewell'
Silent people putting blackout on their windows

I can hear . . .
Sad sobbing of mothers
Booming of the bombs
Roaring of the huge buildings falling
Quietness all around me
Sounds of scared evacuees crying

I can feel . . .
Enemy attacks from above
Dad fighting in the war
Scared to leave my mother
Excited to see the beautiful countryside
Feel my first meadow grass.

Sebastine Okwuolisa (8)
St Margaret Clitherow RC Primary School, Stevenage

World War II

W orld war II has begun.
O ver the trenches and through the mud.
R ats crawling through the trenches.
L obbing bombs through the trenches
D ead people on the floor.

W ar planes dropping bombs.
A rmy are in battle, everybody's dying.
R ed blood spilling down the sewer.

T anks crashing into troops.
W ar has ended.
O n the floor no more.

Fraser Laird (9)
St Margaret Clitherow RC Primary School, Stevenage

World War II From A Child's Eyes

I can see . . .
Big black bombs from the pitch black sky.
Enormous bombs lighting up the sky
As they explode one at a time.
Policemen walking up and down
Making sure we're safe and sound.
Air-raid sirens flashing red and white.

I can hear . . .
The sound of planes flying ahead.
People screaming all around.
My mother saying, 'goodbye dear.'
Trying to contain her tears.
The sound of sirens makes me tired.
You can hear the burning, crackling fire.

I can feel . . .
My mother's tears dripping down me.
My heart is beating as fast as a drum.
Tears running down my cold cheek.
It hurts me as I say goodbye.

Harriette Ridgers-Latif (8)
St Margaret Clitherow RC Primary School, Stevenage

Henry VIII

Henry VIII was a very strong king
He could give you anything from a chopping off of a head
To a very bad sting,
Anything he wanted he would get,
No he wouldn't
Do you want a bet?

I think Henry loves the taste of blood.
With all the people he has killed
He could have a house flood.

Divorced, beheaded, died,
Divorced, beheaded, survived.

Andrew Gordon-Akpamgbo (9)
St Margaret Clitherow RC Primary School, Stevenage

World War II From A Child's Eyes

I can see . . .
The light of crackling, roaring bombs
Lighting up the dark, night sky
My mum's tears running down her face
Families huddling underground

I can hear . . .
The sound of planes running across the breezy sky
The sound of people running and screeching,
Up and down the streets
The sound of banging, crashing and screeching.
The sound of crying, hard breathing, screaming.

I can feel . . .
The pounding of my mother's heart.
A tear from one of my mother's lovely eyes.
The feeling of the heat up there
London's burning everywhere.
On the train it's very tight,
Hold back my tears with all my might.

Dylan Howard (8)
St Margaret Clitherow RC Primary School, Stevenage

World War II

Bombs drop from enemy planes,
Bursting my ear drums as they explode.
Rattling of machine guns shake the floor,
Bombs exploding please no more.
Parents leaving their children to evacuate.
They look back to see them cry.
A gas bomb is in the trench, everyone take cover.

Planes look spectacular as they barrel roll through the air.
Submarines emerge from the sea firing torpedoes,
Where will they be?
My friends drop down dead,
It's a blood-curdling thought.
Body parts go flying as a grenade is caught.

Steven Elliott (10)
St Margaret Clitherow RC Primary School, Stevenage

Tudors

I've had six wives
Two beheaded, one died
Two divorced and one survived.

Anne Boleyn cheated,
She got executed,
I don't regret it at all.

Her fear was strong
Her sweat was flowing
The blood dripped from her head,
It was the reddest of reds.

I love feasts
People think I am a beast.
But that's just how I am.

I wanted a son,
I got one but he died early on.
That's a shame because my daughter ruled,
And women think it's a game.

Sandra Tofek (11)
St Margaret Clitherow RC Primary School, Stevenage

On The Salty Sea

I see the Jolly Roger waving wildly
I see the golden treasure
I see the cannons ready to shoot
I see the battlefield!

I hear the guns shooting loudly
I hear the wild wind!
I hear the ocean roaring!

I smell the captain's dinner which is bacon and eggs
I smell the sea when the pirates drink their tea!

I feel hungry for the captain's dinner
I feel like fighting when I am writing
I feel seasick when I am on the sea.

Emily McTait (7)
St Margaret Clitherow RC Primary School, Stevenage

Ancient Egypt

In Ancient Egypt tombs, I had butterflies in my tummy,
And as I ventured through the mist I really wanted my mummy.
I tried to think of a cute, fluffy, little bunny
But something here thinks I'm yummy.

I saw a faint light and it lead
To a tall figure that towered over my head.
The pharaoh filled with fury and rage said
'Who dares make me get out of my bed?'

Trembling in fear and horror, I ran out of his sight.
It was dark, dull and cold. Midnight.
I couldn't see a thing and there wasn't any light.
As I kept moving forward I saw the shadow of the Sphinx, tall and high.

In a deep, loud voice it said, 'What is your name?'
Frightened and terrified I replied, 'Sh-sh-Shane.'
In the same deep voice the Sphinx said, 'So Shane, what is your game?'
My voice echoed through the air when I said, 'I need a place to stay, please
don't think I'm insane.'

Mevanti Fernando (10)
St Margaret Clitherow RC Primary School, Stevenage

World War II

Men fighting for their lives
The sound of machine guns
Bombs lighting up the night sky
Thick smoke flying everywhere
The sound of planes overhead dropping bombs everywhere
Houses on fire, if not fallen down
Burnt to shreds
It seems to last forever
Day after day it's getting worse
I just want it to stop
People wailing in the streets
Orphans crying at the sound of bombs
Men coming home, wounded, shot in the leg or arm
I want it to stop!

Jason Haley (10)
St Margaret Clitherow RC Primary School, Stevenage

Cleopatra

When
I go out
Side, I see
My slaves
Making my
Glorious Sphinx
And pyramids.
The smell of sweat
And camels is the most
Disgusting smell.
I just hate the sound of
Moaning and groaning of my
Slaves. I love being rich
And having all these servants.
I love my golden crown and jewellery.
Even though I'm a pharaoh, I am
Not a man or wearing that awful
Beard. Now be gone!

Lauren Simpson (10)
St Margaret Clitherow RC Primary School, Stevenage

WWII

Bombs lighting up the sky
Spitfires flying
Blood soaring through the sky
Tanks firing
Air-raids waking people
The sound of Hitler screaming
Roars of the soldiers fighting for their lives
Guns firing
The whistles of trains as loud as guns
Freezing trenches
Wondering about families
Sore feet from the trenches
Heart pounding
Hopefully no World War III.

Scott Fitzpatrick (9)
St Margaret Clitherow RC Primary School, Stevenage

World War II From A Child's Eyes

I can see . . .
Bombs exploding in the dark sky.
People running for their lives.
London's burning bombs are falling.
Bombs zooming, people shaking.

I can hear . . .
Babies screaming, dogs barking.
Mothers sobbing it will be alright.
The train whistling as it pulls up.
Children crying, fire burning.

I can feel . . .
Mother's warm hand soft and wrapped around me.
Butterflies in my tummy waiting to be unleashed.
The sadness all around the train.
The nerves make me need the toilet,
Who is there?
Who is there?

Cara Kinsella (8)
St Margaret Clitherow RC Primary School, Stevenage

World War II From A Child's Eyes

I can see . . .
People fighting in the air.
Planes are bombing everywhere.
Big black bombs whooshing through the sky.
Some are bombing in the air.

I can hear . . .
Sirens wailing to warn the people enemy planes are coming.
Children screaming all around.
Mothers crying, saying farewell.

I can feel . . .
Butterflies in my tummy.
I can feel my mum's tears on my hand.
My hands are shaking nervously.

Oliver O'Brien (8)
St Margaret Clitherow RC Primary School, Stevenage

139

World War II From A Child's Eyes

I can see . . .
Enemy planes clattering and clunking as they swoop past
The big black bullets shooting the German show offs
People rushing to the station
Next it is my turn
Mothers weeping as the bucket of bolts leaves

I can hear . . .
Bombs exploding all around me
All I can hear is mothers crying
People sleeping and smoking on the train
The children sobbing on the train
It is silent all around

I can feel . . .
My sister clutching my hand
Mum waving farewell
My sister pulling my hair
The train clutches to a halt.

Christopher Speight (9)
St Margaret Clitherow RC Primary School, Stevenage

A Jolly Roger

A Jolly Roger waving in the air:
Cannon balls
Floating in the air
Pieces of wood
Blown off an enemy ship.

The sunken wreck of a ship:
Scattered coins
On the seabed
Old skeletons.

Pirates waving
On an island
Shouting for dear life
Treasure somewhere around.

Oliver Brady (8)
St Margaret Clitherow RC Primary School, Stevenage

World War II From A Child's Eyes

I can see . . .
Huge bombs cracking in the pitch-black and smoking sky.
Big, black bullets ready to be put in the dangerous black guns.
Mothers holding in their tears while the children leave.
Blacked out windows which I will miss.
A little brown teddy that I always kiss.

I can hear . . .
The whooping of air-raid sirens.
People screaming as the bombs dropped
My heart thumping dramatically while I worry.
The train tracks fiercely slowing down with sparks.

I can feel . . .
Tears all down me from my mum.
My mum holding my hand on the train.
Wet tears on my seat from sobbing so much.
My little sister tugging on my yellow coat,
Asking for more kiss.

Megan Warren (8)
St Margaret Clitherow RC Primary School, Stevenage

The Ship

Cannonballs flying like Frisbees.
Lifeboats pushed like a toy car.
Handkerchiefs falling like rocks.
Pirates fighting with cutlasses.

Boom!
Splash!

A shark.
A pirates' ship sinking.
Fire!
Danger!
Sharks coming!
Gunpowder, smoke!

Damian Wolfram (7)
St Margaret Clitherow RC Primary School, Stevenage

World War II From A Child's Eyes

I can see . . .
Enemy soldiers firing rounds.
Bombs exploding nearby, mums screaming, 'Get inside!'
London burning to the ground, smoke everywhere,
Mothers crying, weeping, deeply upset.
Enemy planes diving down shooting everything,
Glass smashed and people crying with fear.

I can hear . . .
Mothers weeping painful tears kissing their kids farewell.
Air-raid sirens screeching a warning attack.
London burning, crackling, smoking.
Policemen shouting, 'Black out, enemy planes coming!'

I can feel . . .
The pain inside my heart as I'm being evacuated.
The cold tears of my mum as she is weeping.
I feel the warmth in my mum's arms as she says goodbye.
My dad saying goodbye, maybe forever?

Rian O'Brien (8)
St Margaret Clitherow RC Primary School, Stevenage

Jack The Ripper

Jack the Ripper, oh Jack the Ripper,
He really was the biggest killer,
He's the biggest English mystery,
And definitely part of history

Creeping around in deserted streets,
Killing people in massive heaps,
Parents keeping their children near,
The tapping feet is what you can hear

The dreaded sound of a blood-thirsty knife,
A killer making people lose their life,
Distant screams and cries for others,
A man that never was a lover.

James Hunter (10)
St Margaret Clitherow RC Primary School, Stevenage

World War II From A Child's Eyes

I can see . . .
Bombs lighting up the dark smoking sky and Germans flying,
It is not a good sight
Dripping tears go down my face and people running to catch their train
Steam trains going away and my mum giving me my sandwich
My little sister doesn't want to go but my mum says, 'You have to,
It is safer for you there.'

I can hear . . .
Sirens warning to get to safety and mum running to the crowded shelter
Bombs sizzling in the air screaming everywhere it is too much to bear
The howling of my sister and the bumping of the train
The windows opening and closing and the wind fluttering

I can feel . . .
The nervousness and pain of everyone
My strong heart breaking and turning into stone
The memory of my mum and dad
The sadness of me and the tears of my dad.

Ugonna Umunnakwe (8)
St Margaret Clitherow RC Primary School, Stevenage

WWI

The planes flying above my head.
I knew that I would soon be dead!
This war would not turn out clean,
The soldiers that couldn't be seen.

People running and crying,
Soldiers shooting and dying,
Mum and Dad charging to the bomb shelter,
They wouldn't let me save my helter skelter.

The train that choo-chooed away,
People didn't say hooray.
Sad little faces waving goodbye,
The parents said at least they won't die.

Zara McTait (9)
St Margaret Clitherow RC Primary School, Stevenage

World War II From A Child's Eyes

I can see . . .
Families huddling in the dark, some in air-raid shelters, some in mud.
Mothers trying not to cry, cuddling their children, saying good luck my boy.
Injured people on the ground.
People running all around.
Houses burning all around
Spitting and crackling awfully loud.

I can hear . . .
The clanking and the rattling of the steam train going.
The rattle of machine guns shooting the bullets.
The sound of firemen with the hose putting the fire out.
People running, people screaming everywhere as well as people that are injured.

I can feel . . .
My sister's heart pounding and her silent tears running down my arm.
The pain of my sister's tiny broken heart.
The butterflies in my stomach trying to be excited about my new home.
The warmth of mum's hug and kisses goodbye.

Tiffany Clark (8)
St Margaret Clitherow RC Primary School, Stevenage

The Tudors

People scream when the axe has killed
Blood that squirts and spills
Celebration here and there
That there would be no villains anywhere.

A big long table filled with lots of delights
More than you can ever eat
It was amazing at the sight
Soup, bread, vegetables and lots of meat

Henry was a very mean king
One day he died, sing, sing
He was very fat, a disease
Well, that's what we believe.

Saffron Foley (9)
St Margaret Clitherow RC Primary School, Stevenage

WWII

Guns firing
People dying
Spitfires crashing
When will it end?

Hitler screaming at his men
Let's send Britain back to their den
Missiles crashing
When will it end?

Air-raid sirens flashing all around
Here comes the missile with a sound
Bomb shelters rattling
When will it end?

Gas masks saved the war
Everything back to normal I'm sure
No more blood or gore
Hopefully no more.

Callum Kent (9)
St Margaret Clitherow RC Primary School, Stevenage

What A Life

I'm trudging through the wind and rain.
I can't go on, I'm full of pain.
Bullets flying past my ear.
The lads around me are full of fear.
Agony and spasm take over men's voices.
Bangs and booms are the only noises.
Along with the screeching, machine-gun fire.
Jimmy says he likes the deafening sound, the little liar.
German bombs dropping here and there.
Trying to find the British lair.
Rats are playing hide-and-seek.
But I've seen 13 already this week.
At the moment I'm sitting on a wooden bench.
Trying not to inhale the awful stench.
What a life.

Alex Ridgers-Latif (10)
St Margaret Clitherow RC Primary School, Stevenage

Tudor Life

My Tudor school is a pain
Afraid of getting whipped by the cane
Finally my day is done
The chance of surviving to five is second to none

King Henry loved beheading, blood it's a bliss
Time for justice
I am very strong and good with my fist
I will send you into the mist

My father has died
People say football, I hide
Because that was how my father died, isn't that a foul?
Every night I hear the wolves howl

Gold and silver is what they drink
But poor people don't have a sink
Rich people have a feast
But poor have to kill a beast.

Josh Crawford (11)
St Margaret Clitherow RC Primary School, Stevenage

Shipshape And Piratey

The seagulls squawking over my head.
The cannonballs attacking other ships!
The stupid scallywags on my ship!
The horrible fishes in the sea.

The chef burning my lovely bacon.
The scent of salty water filling the air.
My yuck yucky breath smells so rotten.
The horrible seagulls poo on my ship.
The sea splashing on my ship.
The bilge pumping up and down.
My treasure going left and right.

The harsh breeze brushing against my cheeks.
The ship rolling up and down.
My scallywags jabbing me, I hate it.

Aële Eyong Ebai (7)
St Margaret Clitherow RC Primary School, Stevenage

World War II

I hear . . .
Drills of machine guns firing
Planes flying overhead
Bombs exploding

I see . . .
Men falling and mouthing, *I love my family*
Grey skies filled with smoke
Trenches blowing up

I feel . . .
Sweat dripping down my body
Rain getting through the gap of my neck and collar
The pain of my swollen feet

I smell . . .
German gas bombs
Dirty mud rubbed into my clothes
Fuels for planes.

Daniel Luke O'Connor (10)
St Margaret Clitherow RC Primary School, Stevenage

World War II From A Child's Eyes

I can see . . .
My mummy crying while she is packing my little stockings.
Black out windows and hearing the aircraft overhead.
Black bombs come overhead.

I can hear . . .
My mummy crying with big massive tears coming down her face.
Cows mooing on the grass.
My mummy is zipping up my little suitcase.
The siren going on really loudly so I can't concentrate.

I can feel . . .
My heart breaking up into little pieces.
My mummy hugging me with her warm hands.
My mummy crying big tears.
My mummy hugging me.

Grace Knell (8)
St Margaret Clitherow RC Primary School, Stevenage

After The Bomb

Wrecked houses,
Rubble and mess
Is anyone alive?
I'll have to guess

Dead bodies
Flames and fire
Which are leaping
Higher and higher

A foul stench of
Blood and guts
That are spilling
From deep cuts

Spitfire engine
Whirrs and roars
Messerschmitt
Lifts and soars.

Dominic Rory White (9)
St Margaret Clitherow RC Primary School, Stevenage

Pirate

Shiny cannons shooting cannonballs
Pirates running away with our treasure!
Holes in the Jolly Roger's sails,
Wet footprints on deck.

Fish, cheese and chips in the galley.
Feet being used as weapons.
The ocean smell all around.
I smell the captain's dinner.

Parrots squawking, thunder roaring
Lightning crashing, pirates talking

Scared, unhappy and hungry
Frightened and hot

I finally run for the safety of the bilge.

Jessica Kosky (7)
St Margaret Clitherow RC Primary School, Stevenage

9/11 Twin Towers

Hijackers manage to sneak through security
The President is at the school in America
They're boarding the plane, but everyone is clueless
They're ready for take off, up into the air
Innocent passengers watching the trolley being pushed along
Hijackers repeating their plans for the last time
They creep to the cabin door
They threaten the pilots and they give in
Into the cockpit, this is dangerous now
In the south tower they have no idea
They are flying into America,
Army jets are ready for take off
Closer, closer, closer
Kaboom, crash, crash!
People jumping from the windows
Another plane, *crash, bang, wallop!*
It's the Pentagon next, this is Doomsday.

William George Bray (10)
St Margaret Clitherow RC Primary School, Stevenage

My Pirate Poem

A Jolly Roger,
Waving and coughing madly in the wind.
A cannon,
Dark and black firing black cannonballs.

The wind howling,
Like a wolf.
The sea, clashing
Against the dark grey rocks.

The pongy, disgusting fish.
The much stronger, more disgusting stench
Of seagull poo stinking the whole place out!

I feel like,
Someone is betraying us, someone told where the treasure is,
Someone is working for that boat over there.

Dario Brincat (7)
St Margaret Clitherow RC Primary School, Stevenage

World War II From A Child's Eyes

I can see . . .
Bombs dropping from darting planes
Exploding in the dark cold sky
My mum exploding with gentleness and waving goodbye
Enemy planes speeding away from a successful battle
Children crying painful tears.

I can hear . . .
Enemy planes swooping, darting and dodging ally bullets
Huge bangs of bombs lighting up the night sky
Bullets firing fiercely making a loud screeching sound
Children screaming and wailing for their mums

I can feel . . .
Cold tears trickling down my neck
Fear of being attacked by the Germans
Bombs dropping and dirt hitting my face
Crackling fire with red flames.

Sherwin Elliott (8)
St Margaret Clitherow RC Primary School, Stevenage

Attack

Blood drifting
Like leaves falling
Bombs blowing
Up the ship

Cannons firing
Waves hitting and crashing hard!

Salt from the sea.
Smoke from the battle of Germans.
Smelly sardines.

Broken wood.
Angry!
Terrified!
Upset!
Horrified!

Luca Hoffman (7)
St Margaret Clitherow RC Primary School, Stevenage

World War II From A Child's Eyes

I can see . . .
Enemies approaching.
Mum sobbing heart-felt ears.
People running.
Sirens booming louder and louder.
London's burning, buildings are falling
Rapidly around us.

I can hear . . .
Bombs bang, people running for their lives.
Babies screaming red-hot faces.
Policemen shouting, 'Black out your lights!'

I can feel . . .
My teddy hugging me.
My dog jumping up at me.
The fluttering butterflies in my stomach.
The kisses in my ear coming from my mum.

Sophie Allen (8)
St Margaret Clitherow RC Primary School, Stevenage

The War Began

The war began a long time ago
The soldiers marched very slow
There is never a Santa saying, 'Ho, ho, ho!'
Sad little faces come and go
Oh why, oh why, do we never get snow?
People dying, shooting of guns

T he loud sounds of the bombs
H e was scared of all the songs
E ar-aching sirens from the outside pong

W hen I wake I started to shake
A nd so my Mom tells me just to make
R ed cherry fires of warm in my head.

Romilly Proud (9)
St Margaret Clitherow RC Primary School, Stevenage

World War II From A Child's Eyes

I can see . . .
Huge bombs cracking on the ground.
Enemy planes going above the big rocky hills.
New evacuee friends saying hello.
Trains coming to gather children and take them to safety.

I can hear . . .
My mum crying.
The train clunking on the big track.
People shouting, 'Here comes the train.'
Enemy planes roar overhead.

I can feel . . .
My sister's tears on my hand.
My mum giving me a huge hug.
My heart beating like a football
Bouncing on the ground.
Kisses all over me.

Ana Drakes (8)
St Margaret Clitherow RC Primary School, Stevenage

World War II

W orld War II was started by Hitler
O ver the world the soldiers march
R unning parents to save their children
L aunching the bombs from the planes above
D ead people lying on the floor

W ar planes crashing, getting set on fire
A eroplanes flying above the trenches
R ed blood all over the floor

T anks shooting and crashing
W ar is over, soldiers have survived
O n the floor people are dead.

Daniel Loake (9)
St Margaret Clitherow RC Primary School, Stevenage

The Grand Ship

Purple dress swordfish saw other ships.
Shooting cannons at the ship but not her.
But she managed to escape as fast as a cheetah.

Boom! Boom! Cannons black as a blackbird.
'Man the lifeboats!'
Whoosh! Whoosh! The wind blowing in my hair.
Splash! Splash! The water went.
Wave, wave goes the flag.

Rubbish from the sea,
'Yuck!'
Bacon from the kitchen under the water.
The smoke from the cannons.
The bilge, gross as could be.

I felt scared, shocked,
Astonished, worried.

Dayna-Mai Lawlor (8)
St Margaret Clitherow RC Primary School, Stevenage

World War II From A Child's Eyes

I can see . . .
Everywhere burning, crackling and smoking
My mum crying ever so badly, you can see she's trying not to
Massive bombs smashing to the ground
Red lights and sirens hurting my eyes

I can hear . . .
The sweeping of enemy planes overhead
People screaming 'Get in your shelters, turn off the lights quickly!'
The screeching of people running around
My mum shouting and crying, 'Good luck!'

I can feel . . .
My stomach rumbling ever loudly
Loads of sadness and weeping around me
My head hurting so badly from being sad
Very sorry for my brother from how very sad he is.

Benjamin Merry (8)
St Margaret Clitherow RC Primary School, Stevenage

Sea War

A dark grey ship coming
Towards us, flag waving
As dark as space and as big as
A double-decker bus.

Cannons getting ready, next
Boom! Boom, boom, boom, boom!
Battle! Battle beginning and
War is waging.

Seasick smell as smelly as fish sick
And it feels so, so, so, so, so, so, so, so
Wind wish the ship moving.

I feel so weak
But I feel devastated
About all the pirates I have lost.
So I will never forget them ever, ever.

Liam Gow (8)
St Margaret Clitherow RC Primary School, Stevenage

World War II From A Child's Eyes

I can see . . .
People running wild from warning of attack,
Bomb shelters' doors slammed for safety.
People's lives ending from bullets in their chest.
Terror all around.

I can hear . . .
Air-raid sirens roaring, giving signals of attack.
Children crying loudly feeling depressed and afraid.
My mum weeping painfully screaming, 'You must go away!'
Bombs banging loudly, millions of people dying each day.

I can feel . . .
Nerves in my stomach as the train arrives.
Saying farewell to Mum who I might not see forever!
As I get on the train I feel devastated.
Will I ever see my family again?

Dominic Burns (8)
St Margaret Clitherow RC Primary School, Stevenage

154

World War II From A Child's Eyes

I can see . . .
Houses falling to the ground.
Bombs exploding in the dark sky.
Children running from the bombs.
Blacked out windows on every house.

I can hear . . .
The wailing of the air-raid sirens.
The bang of the German bombs.
The whistle of the train.
The crying of mums and children saying goodbye.

I can feel . . .
The tears from my brother's eyes.
The butterflies in my tummy.
The wetness of my mum's tears.
The coldness of my mum's hands.

Jacob Dranse (8)
St Margaret Clitherow RC Primary School, Stevenage

World War II From A Child's Eyes

I can see . . .
Enemy planes flying, people falling out
Bombed houses everywhere
Mum crying, thinking Dad is going to die
Dead people on the floor

I can hear . . .
Everyone crying, waving goodbye
The bombs dropping, *bang!*
The fire burning, *smash!*
The buildings smashing

I can feel . . .
Mum's tears on me
Mum hugging me
My heart breaking
The sparks hitting me.

William Sarenden (9)
St Margaret Clitherow RC Primary School, Stevenage

World War II From A Child's Eyes

I can see . . .
Blacked out windows.
Bombs exploding in the air.
Germans fighting and dropping bombs from the sky.
Germans trying to kill people.

I can hear . . .
The planes flying overhead.
The screaming and crying of the children and the mothers.
The Germans shouting.
The people screaming.

I can feel . . .
The butterflies in my stomach.
The nerves I am feeling.
The aches in my stomach.
The crying coming out of my eyes.

Rhianna Mitchell (8)
St Margaret Clitherow RC Primary School, Stevenage

World War II From A Child's Eyes

I can see . . .
A colourful bomb brightening up the dark, dark sky.
My mum shivering as I wave goodbye.
Everybody crying, everybody sad, everybody making me feel so sad.
Men running into the night
Everybody had such a fright

I can hear . . .
The howling of the sirens telling us to hide.
The planes swooping above us ready to attack.
The people screaming, 'Run! Run! Run!'
The whistling of bombs dropping and people screaming.

I can feel . . .
The tears from my mum's eyes falling onto my chest.
My brother's hands cuddling me with his favourite teddy in his hands
I can feel my heart breaking inside of me.

Joshua Dear (8)
St Margaret Clitherow RC Primary School, Stevenage

World War II From A Child's Eyes

I can see . . .
Big Ben shining in the moonlight.
Enemy planes flying high in the black sky.
My little black puppy that I will miss.
My mum saying farewell, screaming.

I can hear . . .
My heart roar, roar, roaring.
My hands shaking like mad, they're going like they are crazy.
Me sobbing extremely loudly but I'm not the only one.
The big bashing of the bombs going boom, bash.

I can feel . . .
My brother's tears dripping on my hand, drip-drop.
Trains brake, carriages shaking, wheels aching.
Vibrations of bombs dropping dangerously.
Tears tipping down my face.

Darcey Streeter (8)
St Margaret Clitherow RC Primary School, Stevenage

World War II From A Child's Eyes

I can feel . . .
Enormous bombs all around.
Mothers wailing and fainting to the ground.
Noisy planes gliding through the air.
Everyone shouts, look out, beware!

I can hear . . .
Howling air-raid sirens, louder then ever.
Sergeant saying, 'We are fierce, we are clever!'
The Germans are furious and gave a frown.
A private shouted back, 'We will demolish this grey, dull and disgusting town.'

I can feel . . .
My mum giving me a huge hug.
I get on the train and was worried.
I feel like curling up on the floor.
And I hope that Britain wins the fearful war.

Nathaniel Duncan (8)
St Margaret Clitherow RC Primary School, Stevenage

The Environment

E ven animals can die of pollution
N ature will have to find a solution
V egetables, people will not eat
I nstead they kill animals for meat
R esting until they find hope
O nly their souls have been broke
N o more clean at my feet!
M ade from animals into meat
E ven they cannot defeat
N ever trash our planet
T he environment is where we live!

Sarah Teles (9)
St Margaret Clitherow RC Primary School, Stevenage

Henry VIII

Henry, Henry was so fat
He had a beard like a ginger cat
He had many wives
Who lost their lives
He watched the telly
While he was stuffing his belly
When he went to the loo
He got a bit smelly
His favourite food was goose
While we like chocolate mousse!

Lucas Hayhurst (9)
St Margaret Clitherow RC Primary School, Stevenage

How Dinosaurs Became Extinct

Mr Spinosaurus broke his spine.
Mrs Stegosaurus got her head stuck in a pine.
Mr Brachiosaurus got into a fight with Mr Giraffe.
The baby pterodactyl got struck by lightning which made him daft.

Joshua Zulu (10)
St Margaret Clitherow RC Primary School, Stevenage

World War I

Bombs are lighting up the sky
The sound of screaming all the time
Smelling smoke makes me cry

I have lost my mummy
I try to help everybody
But no one lets me so I look for my daddy

I start to cry
Everyone wants to know why
I stop crying and start to sigh.

Tess Moran (9)
St Margaret Clitherow RC Primary School, Stevenage

Pirates

Waves,
An island,
The sails blowing,
Seagulls.

Sharks, fish, octopus.
The wind
Seagulls screeching
Cannonballs.

Cold, wet, mean, scared.

Rachel Hodgskin (7)
St Margaret Clitherow RC Primary School, Stevenage

World War

T he loud sirens in our houses
H eroes hiding and curled up like mouses
E very second people dying

W orld War always keeps you lying
A soldier marching like a cop
R ight this has to stop.

Ellis Bounsall (9)
St Margaret Clitherow RC Primary School, Stevenage

World War II

Bombs light up the night
Soldiers shoot with their machine guns
The shining bullet shines through the sky

Injured soldiers bleeding
The smell of fresh blood
Brings me down to the ground

Soldiers run through the muddy trench
Waiting, for enemies to arrive
Machine guns ready for action.

Jessica Mary Baird (10)
St Margaret Clitherow RC Primary School, Stevenage

World War II

The death rattle of a machine gun,
The bang of a hand grenade,
The cry of wounded soldiers.

Dangerous depressing death,
Although Hitler killed half,
Be aware of the battlefield.

The boom, boom, boom of a tank,
The roar of a Nazi plane,
And the pain of a bullet.

George Allen (10)
St Margaret Clitherow RC Primary School, Stevenage

World War II

Soldiers falling to the ground,
The smell of flesh in the soldier's trench,
Maybe you will be next in line.

My machine gun in my hand,
Maybe it is an air-raid,
Days are gone, the tanks have bombed.

People staying in bomb shelters,
People screaming their heads off,
Watch out, it could be you.

Cameron Krogh (9)
St Margaret Clitherow RC Primary School, Stevenage

Gladiator

G olden sand stained dark crimson.
L aughter and cheering all around me.
A rmour scratched and helmets dented.
D eath is in the air.
I f you come across a gladiator, run and hide.
A fraid of getting killed.
T earing flesh.
'O hh, ahh' shouted from the crowd.
R ome, it's such a dangerous place.

Isabella Hopcraft (9)
St Margaret Clitherow RC Primary School, Stevenage

Egyptian Mummies

M ummified in coffins
U nion in groups
M arvellously still
M agnificent on display
I maginative in their dreams
E lectrifying and rich
S trong and hungry.

Jordan Clark (10)
St Margaret Clitherow RC Primary School, Stevenage

World War II

War, war, war was the worst thing I saw,
Firing and dying all around,
Mothers crying of evacuation,
Seeing their children waiting at the station,
What a sad moment for all,
What an evolution war,
Will just have to find itself a solution,
Please Lord let the war end,
So that men have better time to spend.

Natasha Pettine Ramirez (9)
St Margaret Clitherow RC Primary School, Stevenage

The Battle Of 9/11

Blood flying, people dying
Bullets firing, people screaming
Bodies lying, pale and cold
Dead people, look like they're going to mould

Blazing hot fire, snapping like gunshots,
Bombing noises everywhere
Fire as bright as the sun and as hot
Most people were so scared.

Roan Shea Pemberton (9)
St Margaret Clitherow RC Primary School, Stevenage

Soldier

Thump of feet, rat-a-tat of machine guns
Screams of the wounded
Whoosh of bullets racing past my face
Peeew, bang! The sound of bombs striking
The cold wind hitting my bare face
Agony fills my body
Because of the bullet that just struck me
Proudness overcomes me because I'm fighting for my country.

Hannah Ridgers-Ashton (10)
St Margaret Clitherow RC Primary School, Stevenage

World War I

Bombs flying through the sky, everybody is going to die.
Guts and blood everywhere, there are guns over there.
Soldiers dying, enemies killing,
The choppers are destroying, the enemies are annoying
What's going on in the world?
We got bombs hitting, we're not fitting, in our RC cars
There's nukes coming down
We'll have a frown, when it hits.

Max Ellington (9)
St Margaret Clitherow RC Primary School, Stevenage

Soldier

S tanding at the front line praying that this isn't your last day
O ut in the open, fighting for survival
L onely, heart pumping, ten beats a second
D istance around you, enemies can be anywhere
I wait for my enemy to appear
E nemy planes above me, I shake while I wait
R espect the ones whose lives have left us.

Gabi Drury (10)
St Margaret Clitherow RC Primary School, Stevenage

World War II

S oldiers sounds of pain echo through the trenches.
O ncoming planes roar through the sky all day and all night.
L etters from families coming in every week
D ead bodies lay on the battlefield as injured men struggle back
I njuries are coming into medical rooms
E choes in the trenches of orders from the trenches
R eloading of guns in my ear drums.

Kieran Graves (11)
St Margaret Clitherow RC Primary School, Stevenage

Ancient Greece

Greek soldier footsteps pounding against the floor,
The sound of swords swinging and body parts all over the damp, muddy ground
The smoky smell of the dragon's fiery breath
The clinging sound, as two swords clash together.
Shining armour, blinded by the light
Arrows soaring through the sky and shields guarding the soldiers.
Spears pointing in the air.

Charlie James Mcglynn (10)
St Margaret Clitherow RC Primary School, Stevenage

Soldier

S tanding on the edge of existence
O n the run to defend your country
L eave your family and friends
D eath's door at your face
I watch my best friend die right before my eyes
E nemies attack me
R ampage through a trench.

Luke Palmer (10)
St Margaret Clitherow RC Primary School, Stevenage

Rainforest

As the wind blows hear the trees rustle
Listen to the birds singing
The animals scurrying around looking for food
And the rushing sound of the water falling down
I love watching the stream hitting the rocks
It's amazing how far the tree frogs can leap
And length of the chameleon's tongue.

Olivia Andrews (10)
St Margaret Clitherow RC Primary School, Stevenage

World War II From A Child's Eyes

I can see . . .
People fighting out of my window.
Bombs falling from planes.
People running to the air-raid shelter.
Lots of blackout windows.

I can hear . . .
Sirens going off and bombs exploding.
Bombs shooting off into the sky.
Bombs banging and people running.
Children screaming around the train.

I can feel . . .
Butterflies in my tummy.
I can feel my mum's tears dripping down me.
My mum giving me a hug before I go.

Grace Gilbert (8)
St Margaret Clitherow RC Primary School, Stevenage

Untitled

What can I see?
People holding each other with fright,
Buildings exploding wildly,
Aeroplanes swooping madly overhead
Dropping their deadly loads,
Air raid shelters overflowing.

What can I hear . . . ?
Screaming children running in horror,
Bombs dropping loudly,
My heart pumping silently,
Pressure being made.

What can I feel?
Bugs swarming around my shoes,
Mud feeling soggy,
Shaking ground rumbling,
My mum's hand shaking and holding me tight.

Olivia Cotgrave (8)
Tower Primary School, Ware

WWII

What I can see . . .
In the city of rubble and disaster,
Fires engulf the roads,
Blood spills from the bodies of the dead
And people hide in Anderson shelters,
Nobody would ever be sure
That they were safe anywhere now.

What I can hear . . .
The bombs shatter houses
Like a hot knife through butter,
The wet mud squelching underneath my feet,
Screaming air raid sirens,
The distant cries of the condemned
And the Doodlebugs making their
Distinctive humming noise.
The one that struck fear into the hearts of men.

What I can feel . . .
The cold mud that sinks under my weight,
Blood and tears trickling softly down my face,
The unpleasant warmth of the raging fires
Only a few metres away,
The impact of the bombs, shaking the earth,
The ice-cold metal top of the tiny Morrison shelters
And that frozen, unmistakable emotion that is fear.

Joseph Clark (10)
Tower Primary School, Ware

The Blitz

Falling buildings tumbling together,
Fire blizzards spreading from house to house.
Fires glow in the night sky and fill the air.
You can see adults and children in a corner of a shelter.
In the distance you can hear bombs destroying the city of London.
Warning sirens going off and children and babies crying.

Aimee Thompson (10)
Tower Primary School, Ware

The Blitz

What can you see?
Children crying, looking innocent,
Teardrops falling down their cheeks,
Booming planes, roaring ahead
Scaring mothers with their children,
Burning buildings falling down,
Spreading fires all around.

What can you hear?
Bombs crashing through the misty sky,
Shattering glass falling to bits,
Screaming sirens coming from all around,
Frightening mothers and children.

What can you feel?
Mothers crying because they've lost their sons,
Children puffing from the toxic smoke,
Dampness of the shelter below, wet and cold.

Francesca Jane Smith (11)
Tower Primary School, Ware

World War II

What can I see?
I can see flames thrashing down on cities
And bombs exploding too.
People running so they won't die,
The powerful water smashing down on cities,
The aeroplanes flying to protect cities.

What can I hear?
I can hear cities tearing apart and people screaming,
Sirens ringing and the Germans rushing to attack Britain.
The heavy, strong wind whooshing through skies and cities.

What can I feel?
I can feel water dripping on my head
And air rushing through my body.
The blood dropping through my leg.

Naveen Vatti (8)
Tower Primary School, Ware

YoungWriters

World War II

What I can see . . .
Searchlights gleaming in the sky,
Bombs corrupting the city and ripping through buildings,
The civilians dashing to the shelters,
Others risking their lives to save their family.

What I can hear . . .
People screaming with horror,
Soldiers and innocent men getting blown to bits,
The sirens giving a signal to take shelter,
Children crying as tears run down their cheeks.

What I can feel . . .
The squelching mud under my feet as I walk,
Blood slowly dripping down my hands,
My mum holding me tight with love and care,
The smoke on the back of my neck as I cried.

Szymon Bojarczuk (10)
Tower Primary School, Ware

World War II

What can I see?
I can see tears coming from people's eyes,
Mums squeezing their children,
Blackout curtains being drawn,
People's houses being destroyed.

What can I hear?
I can hear aeroplanes flying past,
Bombs being dropped on people's houses,
Doodlebugs making their sounds
Before the big drop of the bombs.

What can I feel?
I can feel blood on my hands,
Mums fainting in disbelief,
The black smoke rushing down my throat,
Wet wood is what is left of my house.

Ellie Taylor (8)
Tower Primary School, Ware

Untitled

What can I see?
Air raids whistling above my head,
Blood dripping from the dead,
Terrified Mum squeezing me tight,
Smoke and darkness all through the night.

What can I hear?
From every direction a screeching sound
And bloodcurdling screams from all around,
Fires roaring wherever you go,
Bombs keep dropping so and so.

What can I feel?
Smoke and darkness fills the air,
Mothers hugging with love and care,
War has stopped and happiness has spread,
Wonderful feelings in your head.

Sue Holloway (10)
Tower Primary School, Ware

Untitled

What I can see . . .
Searchlights gleaming brightly overhead
Careful, a bomb might give you a fright
Rubble fills the streets
Erupting bombs smashing through windows

What I can hear . . .
Burst pipes spitting water over everyone
Some people screaming loud everywhere
Guns firing so far at planes
Sirens going out to for safety

What I can feel . . .
Cold, damp floor all gooey and sludgy
All of the frights are so shaky than ever
Tears dropping from everyone's eyes
Wishing the war would end.

Hannah Cockman (9)
Tower Primary School, Ware

Untitled

What I can see . . .
Bombs falling from above,
Searchlights flashing in the dark as the Blitz goes on,
Fire eating the buildings,
Bombs ripping through buildings.

What I can hear . . .
Screaming as people run through smashed houses,
Aeroplanes flying through the sky dropping bombs,
Fire engines spitting water out rapidly at burned houses,
Guns shooting at innocent people.

What I can feel . . .
Mum holding me tight,
Mud squelching beneath my feet,
Coldness making me shiver,
My heart beating so fast like a cheetah running.

Daniel Stokes (9)
Tower Primary School, Ware

The Second War

What can I see?
Bombs dropping from above,
Tears running down the cheeks of frightened people,
Fire eating up houses as firemen battle on,
Dust flying everywhere.

What can I hear?
Terrifying screams from mothers as doodlebugs went over,
Bombs exploding on wrecked buildings,
Cold water splashing on steaming fire,
Guns shooting in the hearts of innocent people.

What can I feel?
Adults squeezing me tight,
Squelching, watery mud beneath my feet,
The ground shaking with vibration like it's an earthquake,
Scratchy scars and blood on my hands.

Naima Abdul (8)
Tower Primary School, Ware

Blitz

What can I see?
Glimpse of a destructive plane,
Torture of families outside,
Gunshots from the anti-aircraft guns,
Fire burning down the houses of innocent civilians.

What can I hear?
Bombs whistling like a kettle on a stove,
Metal smashing from the bombs in the misty night,
Sirens wailing to save the lives of many people,
The crackling of fire on the candle behind me.

What can I feel?
The thick, black smoke going down my lungs,
The wet wood on my hands splintering them,
Mud squelching under my feet through the holes in my soles,
My heart racing, ready to stop when the bombers go away.

David Ayers (10)
Tower Primary School, Ware

The Fear

Glimpse of light in the shelter,
Flickers of light in the corner of my eye,
Planes steaming overhead,
Bombs dropping down onto the ground,
Smoke from a building, a blaze of fire

Bomb whistling like a kettle,
Whipping through the smoky air,
Hearing my own heart pound,
Glass shattering on the rubble,
Screams coming from agonised, innocent men,
Sirens warning the men of danger

Feeling the smoke in my chest,
Mud squelching in-between my feet,
My mum's hands holding me tight for dear life,
I could feel a drop of water dripping down my back.

Lewis George Thomas (10)
Tower Primary School, Ware

Untitled

What can I see?
I can see bodies of the dead
Bombs being dropped on innocent children and adults
Soldiers with their guns trying to save us.

What can I hear?
I can hear whistling planes going over the boom shelter
Over and over again
My heart pounding
Mothers and children screaming

What can I feel?
I can feel blood dripping down my face
Mud squelching in-between my feet
I can feel the fear in the people around me.

Ellie Sheen (9)
Tower Primary School, Ware

Untitled

What do I hear?
Bombs smashing and destroying all in their way,
Anti-aircraft guns shooting and exploding,
Roaring planes falling down.

What do I see?
People, young and old, running in fear of their lives,
Bombs shattering everything we loved,
Mums crying and cuddling their children.

What do I feel?
The damp, screechy mud beneath my feet,
The cold air tickling my bones,
The sorrow and sadness of the men we've lost.

Ricardo Olender (10)
Tower Primary School, Ware

Untitled

What can I hear?
The aeroplanes whizzing past my house
Bombs exploding like a grenade
The warden blowing his whistle

What can I see?
My mum on the floor
Men and women running around
My house on fire

What can I feel?
The blood on my hand
My mum holding onto me
The wet wood that is left of my house.

Solomon Knight (9)
Tower Primary School, Ware

Untitled

What can I see?
A flickering candle hanging from the roof,
Scared families huddling together,
Tears trickling down the children's faces.

What can I hear?
The screams of frightened and injured people,
Crackling fires destroying the city,
Exploding bombs demolishing buildings.

What can I feel?
My heart pounding inside my body,
Vibrations of the bombs landing,
Soft, oozy mud beneath my feet.

Aidan Compton (10)
Tower Primary School, Ware

Untitled

What can I see?
Buildings on fire round the people
And my house getting burnt

What can I hear?
Girls screaming at the bombs
Winds shattering and destruction of bombs dropping

What can I feel?
The blood dripping down my leg
I am shivering.

Max Guest (9)
Tower Primary School, Ware

Untitled

Buildings being destroyed by the enemies' bombs,
Smoky, frightening, black skies shining down to the ground,
Fire raging, like a bull charging through people's homes.

Sirens saying 'Help!' because of the dreadful noise of bombs dropping,
Children crying and the soldiers shouting, saying, 'Get to safety,'
The voices of the enemies in planes calling 3, 2, 1, *drop!*

The ground vibrates and rumbles,
Your skin is hot like a volcano,
Your heart races and you jump when the bombs drop.

Katie-Alana McClory (10)
Tower Primary School, Ware

9/11 Destruction

Bang! A sudden thud,
The tower vibrated.
Everybody ran in panic
And headed for the escape route.
It was too late, the biggest thud
Than the first hit the tower.

As the rubble came down
Like a control demolition
It was so terrifying that people
Ran in such a way
Forgetting their children behind.

President Bush was in Florida that time
He was listening to eight-year-olds
Read a rhyme.
People jumped out of windows
Why do you expect them to stay
Inside and die?

I felt horrified, terrified on that day
When the towers hit the ground
In such a scary way.

Tasnia Mahjaben (9)
West Green Primary School, London

Blitz In Germany

Millions of people rushed by,
They left most of their family members behind.
I couldn't see a thing but I still ran.
Huge buildings fell, killing thousands of people.
It was a bloody battle;
Blood splashed on everyone's clothes leaving a dark red mark.
I stopped and turned around . . .
The battle had taken my family down with them.
I looked around, Germany had gone.
The only thing left was blood and dust.
I had never seen such an ugly view.
My eyes flashed like red lights
When a British soldier walked towards me.
He grabbed me and threw me.
My head hit the ground, my eyes closed.
Was it the end?
When I opened my eyes I was on a train to England.
The British soldier had saved my life?

Ece Aksu (10)
West Green Primary School, London

Greek Myths

On a moonless night,
When the frost is thick,
I slither out very quick.

From ear to ear,
When lightning is to strike,
My stories are carefully whispered
Of gods and creatures alike.

What I provoke,
In my folk,
Is not a normal note.

Am I true?
Am I false?
Can you keep up with pulse?

Ruby Stokes (11)
William Patten Primary School, Stoke Newington

More Than A Vase

A pile of rubble is not my life
It was more than that
I was carried home by the god himself
As he wiped his feet on his welcome mat

I carried water, grain, lightning bolts
I helped carry a world
But when the country was falling
He left me in the cold

I was more than a clay container
Helping the gods was my duty
As I sat on the table
Watching Aphrodite in her beauty

Life in the clouds was amazing
But I could never live up to it
I remember Zeus getting rid of me
As I was decaying bit by bit

Down to the ground I fell
To the dusty, brown dirt
I was lying there broken
Decayed more than hurt

As time passed
'About that vase you will never ever see 'em'
Two thousand years later
I was brought to a museum

Sitting in my case
I don't cause any trouble
I'm a very, very, very
Famous pile of rubble

More than a life
More than a story
More than a vase.

Noah Klein (10)
William Patten Primary School, Stoke Newington

My Life As A Hoplite

I was a terminator who stood on the sand
As I saw my best friend die
My metal and bronze armour
Keeping me alive inside

And as the scorching sun fell on us
We knew this was meant to be
Our independency thrived
Across the enemy sea

And at the end of the day
There was one thing on my mind
The money and all the honour
But most importantly pride

After all this hard work
I needed to get some sleep
For another day of fighting
It had to be deep

The next great day of fighting
I couldn't wait for it
Got up, I pulled my armour on
I needed to prepare a bit

The sun was a ball of fire
Rolling across the sky
I was now ready
For my next enemy to die

This was our last chance
We weren't as graceful as a duck
But now as a great Hoplite
Everyone wished me good luck!

Oliver Krishamma (11)
William Patten Primary School, Stoke Newington

One For The Gods

When I'm happy and the sun is shining,
And every cloud has a silver lining,
That's the kind of day I love,
When the big blue sky is full of doves.

When my lovely Hera comes to me,
Singing a beautiful melody,
She is as happy as can be,
That's the thing with the gods you see.

The very next day when I woke up,
I found myself in a bit of a grump.
Thunder and lightning had struck all night
And all of the gods were having a fight.

Later on when the fight was resolved that afternoon,
I thought about how everything had happened too soon.
Someone had kicked and someone had hit
And somebody kept getting called a twit.

Next, Aphrodite had to get married,
She was in love with no one but Ares.
Later on a fight broke out
And all the men began to shout.

In the end it was up to me,
I chose Hephaistos for Aphrodite.
I have to say he was very delighted,
For he was not one of the men who had fighted.

So here I am drinking juice,
I'm still happy and my name is Zeus.

Hannah Gandy (10)
William Patten Primary School, Stoke Newington

The Dear Shield

I protect them not to die
They say they do it all, that's a big, fat lie
They just wave their arms around about
When they get hit they give an horrendous shout

I lived the day my dear friend the shield
Got harshly dumped on the sandy field
My owner did not realise
And when he got stabbed, it was a big surprise

My next owner was not so nice
His brain was no bigger than a grain of rice
When we started fighting he just ran away
Took me with him and hid in a bunch of hay

Two years passed
I didn't know how long I would last
My left breast plate was very rusty
While my sword was extremely dusty

Two thousand eight hundred years later
A man named Dr Matter
Found my owner's bones along with my precious remains
And preserved in glass tombs it seems we have found our fame!

Alis Bedrosyan (10)
William Patten Primary School, Stoke Newington

Remember The Hoplite!

Hoplites running, many are grunting,
Hoplites stretching, it is fun under the burning sun,
Hoplites wrestling to keep them fighting.

Hoplites wearing helmets that will never break,
Hoplites throwing spears, Hoplites wearing jeans,
Hoplites with swords fighting for their lands.

Some Hoplites are too scared to kill
So they decided to pay the bill.
Fighting in battles is scary and very daring.

James Edwards (10)
William Patten Primary School, Stoke Newington

The Hoplite Story

I rose in the summer morn
I saw my sword beside me
A man ran and I knew he was an outlaw
I trudged down to the training ground to see what would happen

I trained hard in the scorching sun
After training their was a terrible announcement
We were going to battle
I walked home terrified of what I heard

The day came and I was ready
With a sword and shield
I marched to Sparta
The Spartans wouldn't let . . .

So we ran
Arrows came raining down, my only friend was killed
I fought hard for honour and pride
And I killed a man or two

While I was fighting I saw something above
Then I realised what it was
But I couldn't move as swiftly as a dove
Moments later I fell with a bang and a thump.

Saihaan Zabir (10)
William Patten Primary School, Stoke Newington

Last Night In WWII

Last night I saw the city,
Flying of the bombs flying down on the city,
Exploding on the town and flying down.

Last night I saw the city,
Roaring like a lion in a cage
Gobbling up another lion.

Last night I saw the city
Winning like a lion
And other animals freed from their cages.

Paulina Mierzejewska (8)
William Patten Primary School, Stoke Newington

The Spear

I am a spear,
And I live here
In a lab in London.

I was dug up in Greece,
At last, I was released
From the hardened soil.

I remember fighting
In the sweltering heat,
It was the Persians we had to defeat.

And when the Greeks won,
I was hugged, I was spun,
But eventually left to lie in the sand.

The 2,500 years lying there went slow,
It blew, it shone, then rain, then snow,
But I was rescued a year ago.

Now I sit with my friend the test tube
And we sit and stare
Into the open air.

Anna Tewungwa (10)
William Patten Primary School, Stoke Newington

Last Night In World War II

Last night I saw the city crumbling
Houses fading away
Bombs whistling down with a *bang!*
Sirens like mad, crying babies.

Last night I saw the city cracking
Bombs crushing down like wild, barking, mad dogs
Fire dancing across roads.

Last night I saw the city cheering
People laughing, kids dancing
Dogs barking mad, look over there,
There was my grandad.

Rajan Singh Rathore (8)
William Patten Primary School, Stoke Newington

Last Night In World War II

Last night I saw the city burning
Like the whole city in a cage of fire
Planes crashing, bang, crash, buildings collapsing
Bombs throwing themselves, flames flying everywhere.

Last night I felt the city dying
Great mounds of bombs being thrown in
Streams of orange and red burning and glowing white hot
And the crumbling ground vanishing beneath my feet.

Last night I heard the city weeping
Raindrops of flames hitting houses that are blazing with fire
Rushing people getting to safety
Roads gaping with cracks.

Last night I saw the city celebrating
People dancing and waving their flags
People dancing, playing and partying
People rushing around and being happy
And that is happening because the war has ended.

Finn Fitzgerald McShane (8)
William Patten Primary School, Stoke Newington

Last Night In World War II

Last night I saw the city's sorrow
Bombs dropping everywhere
And planes zooming over my head
Flashlights up in the sky.

Last night I saw the city blazing
Buildings crumbling down
Trees on fire, knees knocking
As people go into the shelter.

Last night I saw the city cheering
People dancing in the street
VE Day is here
The war is over, we have won.

Ezra Vincent-Townend (8)
William Patten Primary School, Stoke Newington

Last Night In World War II

Last night I saw the city crying,
Big teardrops of bombs fell to the burnt ground,
Large bangs filled the air as the bombs fell,
As innocent people fled to safety.

Last night I saw the city blazing,
Dim orange flames surrounded me,
The white-hot ashes filled my eyes,
As I ran from the bombs.

Last night I saw the city bleeding,
Flares fell like fireworks,
People wept as they fled from their homes,
Burning and crackling down.

Last night I heard the city cheering,
People peering out from their shelters,
At the party streamers fell around,
The war had ended and the party had started!

Tabitha Eason (8)
William Patten Primary School, Stoke Newington

Last Night In World War II

Last night I saw the city burning
Sirens whistling, bombs bombing down
The red flames and ashes going to houses
Slowly, ruby-red, crimson fire.

Last night I saw the city burning
Crimson fire bombs stuck in the ground
Bombing around stabbing and killing people
Houses bombing down with holes.

Last night I saw the city cheering
Lots of people shouting and waving
People smiling and having fun
Happy because the war is won.

Yusuf Mulla (8)
William Patten Primary School, Stoke Newington

Last Night In World War II

Last night I saw the city dying
Flames burst out into dark, foggy gusts of smoke,
Bang, boom, crash!
Out came thunderous bombs.

Last night I heard the city pounding,
People's hearts thumping like drums.
Bang, bang, bang!
'Is it all over?' people cried.

Last night I felt the city trembling,
People's belongings falling to pieces,
Feeling frightened but not giving up,
Come on, we can win the war!

Last night I tasted the city feasting,
People waving flags for joy,
Eating all over again,
'We have won the war!'

Molly Tanner (8)
William Patten Primary School, Stoke Newington

God Of Gods

I feel proud to be the god of gods
I've got control of the weather
My other gods have special powers
I have lightning coming out of my finger.

I feel proud to be the god of gods
My dad tried to eat me
But thankfully my mother saved me
And I feel really proud to wear the crown.

I am as a bull
Charging down the mountainside
My eyes fierce and full
I am my people's guide.

Sameer Patel (10)
William Patten Primary School, Stoke Newington

185

Last Night In World War II

Last night I saw the city blazing,
Bombs dropped with a crash,
Smoke filled the dirty air,
And orange sparks fell speedily.

Last night I smelt the city burning,
Firemen sprinted uncontrollably,
Shelters were crashed from the Blitz,
And tranquil places could no longer exist.

Last night I heard the city crying,
Planes flew all over the place,
Massive bombs crashed into quarters,
And flares fell like fireworks.

Last night I saw the city celebrating,
Everybody cheered in euphoria,
Nothing was pitch-black anymore,
Buildings were built back up, tall and stronger than before.

Rinesa Neziri (8)
William Patten Primary School, Stoke Newington

Last Night In World War II

Last night I saw the city,
Glass shattered like an earthquake,
People cried, 'Please save us!' helplessly,
Black smoke filled the air.

Last night I saw the city falling,
Bombs fell like a falcon going for its prey,
The sirens were whirring loudly,
Big bombs blasted from aeroplanes.

Last night I saw the city celebrating,
With giant flags everywhere,
The people had smiles on their faces,
People were crying with joy.

Ali Sadiq (8)
William Patten Primary School, Stoke Newington

My Life As Cerberus

Why doesn't anyone feed me?
That second head had better watch his neck
He gets all the food he wants while kicking me
He is so lucky, he goes on the deck

I don't like the other ones
But they don't like themselves
So I said, 'Let me be in charge, guys!'
Then they shot themselves

A prisoner, that's what I am
My bed like a metal call
I am made to watch souls all day
Carrying their pots
I am and will be a slave

The moon is a ghostly head
Among the ghostly dead
In our massive head.

Iason Sofos (10)
William Patten Primary School, Stoke Newington

Last Night In World War II

Last night I saw the city flaming
The sky bombed
A field of burning lava-red poppies
The ground trembles.

Last night I heard the city scream
Birds of prey fly over houses
People can smell the dust of smoke
People crying.

Last night I saw the city cheering
People having a beautiful time
People dancing with dogs
Mums kissing their lovely children.

Te'Qun David-McKenzie (8)
William Patten Primary School, Stoke Newington

Last Night In World War II

Last night I saw the city defenceless
People running from the bombs
Underground stations absolutely crowded
People are scared stiff, the Germans have a cunning plan

Last night I saw the city smoking
Buildings flaming like ruby-red pearls
People going to shelter in cellars
Buildings thundering down on top of cars

Last night I saw the city bleeding
Blood rushing down gutters like rain flowing by
Doctors attend to the awfully wounded people
People are moaning like buzzing bees.

Last night I saw the city celebrating
People awarding bravery medals to people
Peace has finally come
People have finally overcome the fear of war.

Bailey Viinikka (9)
William Patten Primary School, Stoke Newington

Last Night In World War II

Last night I saw the city swooping in the dark sky,
People screaming, people doing crimes,
Bombs crashing on top of houses,
Glowing lights in the sky.

Last night I saw the city flaming in the underground station,
Bombs burning in the house,
Ruby-red blood, orange burning fire,
Blood and fire, blood and fire everywhere.

Last night I saw the city laughing,
Singing, having a joyful time,
Waving and celebrating, enjoying
VE Day.

Estelle Davis (8)
William Patten Primary School, Stoke Newington

Last Night In World War II

Last night I saw the city dying,
People screaming, people crying.
Watching people dying.
A ruby-red glow in the distance because a fire is lit.

Last night I heard the city crumbling,
Buildings collapsing.
Streets dying, people sobbing.
There is no longer a pretty path to walk through.

Last night I saw the city injured,
People dying.
Hit in the dreadful bombing moments,
Some didn't make it because their hearts were bleeding.

Last night I heard the city celebrating,
Great gusts of people rushing to have fun.
People dancing, singing, playing, waving and partying,
Because the dreadful war is over.

Eve Fisher (8)
William Patten Primary School, Stoke Newington

Last Night In World War II

Last night I saw the city crashing
Bombs falling down, *crash, crash, boom!*
Exploding like a volcano
Cars crashing and getting too mad with sirens.

Last night I saw the city glowing
Like a field of burning crimson
Tiny town have ignited the world and really
Making people upset and crying with fear and annoyance

Last night I saw the city cheering
People waving flags and celebrating with happiness
Singing and playing with party poppers
Children enjoying themselves.

Nawaal Omar (8)
William Patten Primary School, Stoke Newington

Last Night In World War II

Last night I saw the city dying,
Bombs falling like lightning,
Glowing as bright as stars
And running everywhere.

Last night I heard the city crumble,
Whistles getting louder, stomps everywhere,
Screaming voices getting closer,
Cries of help closing in.

Last night I felt the city crying,
Blood pouring like rain,
Nurses to the pain,
I feel like I'm lost in danger.

Last night I saw the city partying,
Kids dancing all night long,
To the music and song,
Time to celebrate wars gone.

Ella Marsh (8)
William Patten Primary School, Stoke Newington

Last Night In World War II

Last night I saw the city trembling,
Black smoke came from rooftops,
Bombs fell from the freezing sky,
People ran very fast to survive.

Last night I saw the city blazing,
Dive bombers zoomed speedily to the ground,
The cars exploded loudly,
Hot fires burned all around.

Last night I saw the city dancing,
Partying everywhere, people sang,
They were cheering loudly,
They were happy because the war had ended.

Aiman Moossun (8)
William Patten Primary School, Stoke Newington

The Brave Hoplite

I got up in the morning,
Put on my chest plate,
My grieves and my helmet,
I don't want to be too late.

So I marched out of the door,
With my battle gear on,
And I strolled down the road,
But soon I was gone.

I met my mates in the army,
And we raised our swords high,
We marched towards the Persians,
We had to have a try!

My spear and my shield,
Were fighting for the Greeks,
And we beat all of those Persians,
Victory for the Greeks!

Cal Fitzgerald McShane (10)
William Patten Primary School, Stoke Newington

Last Night In World War II

Last night I saw the city crashing,
Thousands of planes bombing cars and buildings,
Children running away and crying, 'Help, help!'
Mums and dads trying to find their kids.

Last night I saw the city watching,
Buildings and trees burning,
People were unhappy, when would this nightmare end?
Bang, bang, bang!

Last night I saw the city cheering,
Fireworks popping everywhere,
People cheering and sharing desserts
Like cupcakes, cakes, ice creams and puddings.

Azad Aydinoglu (8)
William Patten Primary School, Stoke Newington

Last Night In World War II

Last night I heard the city exploding,
Loud bangs were silenced by louder ones,
The city was smoking heavily,
The people were choking under a thick blanket of smoke.

Last night I felt the city heating,
Fires blazing uncontrollably,
Tall as the impossibly high mountains,
Wide as a great sea of fire.

Last night I smelt the city's smoke,
People's precious blood flowing like floods,
The scent of the damp rain,
And the coming of triumph.

Last night I saw the city triumphant,
Peace restored at last,
Citizens were joyful and truly glad,
And celebrating like mad.

Lukas Willers (8)
William Patten Primary School, Stoke Newington

My Life As Cerberus

I don't like the other ones,
But they don't like themselves,
So I said, 'Let me be in charge guys,'
Then they shot themselves.

We don't have bad manners,
We just eat a lot of flesh,
It's time to say goodnight,
So say goodnight guys.

The moon is a ghostly head,
Among the ghostly dead,
In our massive head.

Dexter Gibbs (10)
William Patten Primary School, Stoke Newington

Last Night In World War II

Last night I saw the city sheltering
England raining terror
Buildings cracked like coconuts
Spotlights zooming up.

Last night I sighted the city ablaze
Houses covered in haze
Startled people cold as ice
Planes looming overhead.

Last night I heard the city groaning
Sickbeds a squeeze
Millions dead
A flood of blood in the hospital beds.

Last night I heard the city cheering
Deafening roars of delight thrown to each other
Echoes filling the crowded streets
The sound of sailing flags blowing in the wind.

Oscar Canning-Thompson (8)
William Patten Primary School, Stoke Newington

Last Night In World War II

Last night I heard the city screaming
Bombs falling down and breaking
Fires burning and killing with fear
People trembling like death.

Last night I heard the city dying
People screaming from huge pain
Noisy sirens going on and warning people
People running and screaming for shelter.

Last night I found the city crying
People lost in fiery danger
Buildings burning like freaky flames
Houses breaking and shaking like bombs.

Last night I saw the city dancing
People playing around with laughter
People laughing hilariously
Everyone so happy.

Roxana Sofos (8)
William Patten Primary School, Stoke Newington

Last Night In World War II

Last night I heard the city falling
Crashing broke the silence as the city shuddered
The buildings fell with bangs
Screams sounded on the streets.

Last night I saw the city glowing
Fires ignited in the ruined buildings
Houses crumbled into ashes
Trees lit up to guide the bomber's way.

Last night I heard the city dying
People breathed their last breath
Moans carried through the streets
Some cried, 'Friend or foe?'

Last night I saw the city cheering
English flags waved as balloons flew in the air
Everyone laughed and danced and swayed
Women hugged their men as the children played.

Lara Nettleton (8)
William Patten Primary School, Stoke Newington

Last Night In World War II

Last night I felt the city pounding
Bombs falling down
Screams howling over the wind
Treasures pouring from ruins.

Last night I saw the city's crimson smoke billowing in the sky
Screaming voices filled the air
With exasperating moans
Behind doors, *boom, bang, crash and crack!*

Last night I heard the city dying
Insisting not to stand
Wishing that the Blitz would end
Far sooner it came.

Last night I saw the city laughing
Relief filling its eyes
While trumpets played aloud, victory songs
To roars of delight!

Zoë Edwards (8)
William Patten Primary School, Stoke Newington

Last Night In World War II

Last night I heard the city whistling
Huge planes whizzing through the bright, baby-blue sky
Blazing orange fire glowing like a firefly
Bright yellow light growing up higher and higher.

Last night I saw the city crackling
Big buildings crumbling and crashing down like cracked ice
Tiny and mini running footsteps of little mice
Belongings sadly in a slice.

Last night I saw the city badly injured
Puddles and trails of blood flowing on the deep ground
Bulldogs barking loudly like a werewolf's howl
Fast and zooming hearts like a humungous pound.

Last night I saw the city happily celebrating
Pretty party poppers bursting and sprinkling into the bright skies
No more banging bombs, no more disgusting lies
No more screaming, shouting and baby cries.

Naafiah Ahmed (8)
William Patten Primary School, Stoke Newington

Last Night In World War II

Last night I heard the city whistling
Bombs falling in and breaking
The world was being killed
Houses were eaten by the treacherous bombs.

Last night I saw the city in destruction
Houses blazing in the night air
The planes flying like eagles hunting for prey
I saw hot orange in my eyes.

Last night I felt the city injured
Lying on the dusty ground wailing
Like a deer dying on the forest floor
Planes made for destruction.

Last night I saw the city dancing
Partying in the street, people waving
Children playing
Joy was in the air, the war was done.

Sholto Norman (8)
William Patten Primary School, Stoke Newington

Last Night In World War II

Last night I heard the city getting bombed,
Then bombs came whistling down,
Then *bang!*
The city was gone in flames.

Last night I saw the city screaming,
'Help us, our homes are in flames!'
And they would die too,
Roaring through the city.

Last night I heard the city sirens,
Rushing in and out with people
That were hurt,
Or trembling with fear.

Last night I saw the city partying
With glee that the war was over,
People screaming and loving,
The war was over!

Edie De Burca (9)
William Patten Primary School, Stoke Newington

Last Night In World War II

Last night I heard the city whistling
Lots of people, footsteps running
Into a shelter, screaming, shouting and crying
I was wondering what would happen!

Last night I saw the city glowing
Blazing fires with exploding bombs
I rushed to my parents and saw
Lots of planes with bombs

Last night I felt the city burning
Houses torn away by bombs
People scared to see their houses gone
With gunfire drumming

Last night I thought the city was gone
Fire on top of houses
I was hearing the sound *bang, bang, bang!*
Everything was gone.

Hani Ali (8)
William Patten Primary School, Stoke Newington

Last Night In World War II

Last night I saw the city crumbling,
Buildings dropped in an instant,
Babies screamed and burst into tears,
Children and parents ran to Anderson shelters.

Last night I smelt the city ablaze,
The walls crackled wickedly,
Sparks of bricks flew everywhere,
The sky was bright glowing orange.

Last night I saw the city weakening,
Millions of people died in vain,
Lying on the battlefield so silent,
Family and friends were crying.

Last night I heard the city cheering,
Church bells were a-ringing,
Builders rebuilding buildings,
The nation cried with joy.

Ariella Cigmon-Callor (8)
William Patten Primary School, Stoke Newington

Last Night In World War II

Last night I heard the city fighting
Bombing planes over houses
Gunfire up in the skies
Planes circling over my head.

Last night I saw the city burning with fire
Fire spreading, swarming like ants
Burning houses getting pulled down to the ground
Nothing but ashes are left now.

Last night I felt the city injured
People moaning in terrible pain
People dying all over the place
People desperately trying to stay alive.

Last night I saw the city cheering
Flaming crowds on the street cheering
People waving their English flags
Partying on the street.

Jude Vero (8)
William Patten Primary School, Stoke Newington

Last Night In World War II

Last night I saw the city blazing
Aircraft overloading in the sky
Stars fell like falling sparks
Igniting houses and buildings.

Last night I saw the city shooting
Planes flitted like shadows
In a field of dead poppies
I wished it was just a dream.

Last night I saw the city injured
Oh no! The bombs were dropping
People's belongings fell to the ground
Children had to be evacuated.

Last night I saw the city celebrating
Partying all night
There were no more fights
Everybody could turn on their lights.

Krupali Vassantcumar (8)
William Patten Primary School, Stoke Newington

Last Night In World War II

Last night I saw the city alight
Bombs dropping on houses
People crying in fright
The ear-bursting sound of the siren.

Last night I saw the city exploding
Houses falling down with a *crash!*
Bombs dropping like bullets from a gun
Sounds of people crying in pain.

Last night I saw the city thinking
When will the war stop?
Will it ever stop?
I wish it never happened.

Last night I saw the city hiding
People turning lights off
Frightened of the sound outside
Fire as boiling as lava.

Kit Montague (8)
William Patten Primary School, Stoke Newington

Last Night In World War II

Last night I saw the city cracking
Bombs being dropped down
People running for shelter
Planes flying across London.

Last night I heard the city burning
Houses burning down like sparks
People screaming like crazy
Trees bound to be killed by bombs thumping down on the ground.

Last night I felt the city dying
War falling on me
People feeling heartless
Mums and dads crying for their children.

Last night I saw the city partying
People celebrating in the street party
Children playing in peace without bombs
Families singing and dancing and dogs jumping up at the tables.

Daisy Cappi (9)
William Patten Primary School, Stoke Newington

209

Last Night In World War II

Last night I smelled the city burning,
As hot as the centre of the sun,
I hope this war will soon be over,
Then we will not have to run.

Last night I saw the city ablaze,
Everything was on fire,
We are all tangled up in this giant maze,
There is nothing to admire.

Last night I felt the city sleeping,
Rations were running rapidly low,
Homesick children were weeping,
Though they did not wish to show.

Last night I heard the city cheering,
Lots of streamers filled the streets,
Out of shelters children were peeping,
A big banquet they would finally eat!

Valentina Winship (8)
William Patten Primary School, Stoke Newington

Last Night In WWII

Last night I saw the city crumbling,
Buildings shattered into a thousand parts,
A thousand sparks of Hell itself,
Dug into innocent people's hearts.

Last night I smelled the city flaming,
Thick, black smoke covered pride and joys,
Those people coughed and spluttered,
Germans treated us like toys.

Last night I heard the city moaning,
Many soldiers were in pain,
Most of them eventually passed away,
Whilst the bombing carried on insane.

Last night I heard the city cheering,
For us war was at an end,
The Germans were finally defeated,
There is revenge that we might send.

Charlie Post (9)
William Patten Primary School, Stoke Newington

Last Night In World War II

Last night I saw the city blazing,
Bombs dropping as fast as lightning,
People shouting and screaming,
The fire flames surrounding.

Last night I heard the city crying,
Tears pouring from unhappy eyes,
Their houses were on fire,
Horrible thick, black smoke filled the air.

Last night I saw the city dying,
Blood covered the war ground,
People yelping in pain,
From the monstrous Germans.

Last night I heard the city celebrating,
People cheering with joy,
Fireworks shooting in the air,
Soldiers dancing with relief.

Yunus Unluer (8)
William Patten Primary School, Stoke Newington

Last Night In World War II

Last night I saw the city crumbling,
Bombs dived like shooting stars,
People limped in absolute desperation from warfare,
To escape from the carnage in the air.

Last night I heard the city screaming,
Women and children cried,
As thousands of innocent people died,
As the fires from Hell raged.

Last night I felt the city wrecking,
As buildings crumbled,
To the tattered city floor,
Carrying thousands of people to their deaths.

Last night I saw the city celebrating,
Loads of people ran to the streets,
Everyone went crazy,
Because the war had ended.

Jamie Lindsey (8)
William Patten Primary School, Stoke Newington

Last Night In World War II

Last night I saw the city falling,
Dive bombers zoomed to attack their prey,
People limped in desperation from warfare
To escape from the carnage in the air.

Last night I heard the city cracking,
Sparks fell like flaming rain,
My eyes were filled with nothing but red,
I wished I was just dreaming in my bed.

Last night I smelt the city smoking,
People sped for their lives,
Planes raced across the sky,
I felt a tear come from my eye.

Last night I saw the city partying,
People were drinking and eating feasts,
The sun shone on the beach of Dover
Because now it knew the war was over.

Lonnie Snell (9)
William Patten Primary School, Stoke Newington

Last Night In World War II

Last night I saw the city blazing,
Bombs dropped and split in two,
Setting alight fires, buildings blazing,
Fires caught speedily and black filled the air.

Last night I felt the city shaking,
Planes flew over like vultures in the sky,
Bombs banged down on crumbling buildings,
While many injured people died.

Last night I smelt the city burning,
Sad children got evacuated,
Fires started exploding in towns and cities,
A tranquil city no longer existed.

Last night I heard the city parting,
Colossal parties held everywhere,
Shrieks of laughter filled the air,
Bunting all different colours hung through the streets.

Francesca Habal Maiden (8)
William Patten Primary School, Stoke Newington

Last Night In World War II

Last night I saw the city under attack,
Bombs came whistling down in gangs,
Booming and banging as they came close,
Filling the air with a thick, black smoke.

Last night I felt the city burning,
The force of the bombs as they whizzed past my ears,
It was hot as the sun or more,
Ash fell on my back as I stood and stared.

Last night I smelt the city's smoke,
As I wandered through crowds,
The smell was horrid as can be,
People sprinted around with gas masks.

Last night I heard the city cheering,
'We won! Victory!' they shouted.
People were dancing up the streets
And playing music.

Esme Newnham (8)
William Patten Primary School, Stoke Newington

Last Night In World War II

Last night I saw the city screaming,
Plummeting bombs exploding,
Then the night was alight and lively,
Here we go again.

Last night I smelt the city melting,
Cinders flickered uncontrollably in the air,
All you could see were furious flames,
The night wasn't black anymore.

Last night I heard the calling,
Injured men lay there helplessly,
People knelt over dead bodies weeping,
Many could just stare.

Last night I felt the city cheering,
Confetti drifted down like snowflakes,
Memories would fade,
But the legacy would live on for evermore.

Sidney Josland Diamond (9)
William Patten Primary School, Stoke Newington

213

Last Night In World War II

Last night I heard the city sirens calling,
As everyone scrambled to get inside,
The drone of the planes came nearer,
And the citizens ran to hide.

Last night I saw the city crumbling,
Nearly everything melted down like candles,
People pinned themselves to the ground,
Hearts were thumping in panic.

Last night I found the city groaning,
As if it was in a sort of pain,
You could faintly hear an ambulance coming,
To try and heal all wounds of war.

Last night I felt the city crying victory,
You could see confetti pouring from the sky,
People dancing and having fun,
Singing songs, music and laughter.

Esther Wall (8)
William Patten Primary School, Stoke Newington

Last Night In World War II

Last night I heard the city flaming,
Bombs went crashing down,
Bang! Crash! Boom! People flew to the ground,
Thousands of people died.

Last night I saw the city crying,
Flares went splash on the ground like rain,
People lost all their children,
And they died.

Last night I felt the city shaking,
Bombs went bang! Fires filled the air,
Sneakily, soldiers crouched under houses,
Tanks shot hundreds of people dead.

Last night I heard the city crying,
Fireworks went up like shooting stars,
Hundred of flags filled the city,
A sea of red, blue and white.

Valentin Truman (8)
William Patten Primary School, Stoke Newington

Last Night In World War II

Last night I heard the city gasping,
Explosions and then thick smoke,
Beep! Everyone to their shelter!
We must all pray for hope.

Last night I saw the city in agony,
Bang! Boom! Endless amounts of fire,
Everywhere danger, nowhere safe,
Casualty numbers getting higher and higher.

Last night I felt the city trembling,
Pain and fear covered the land,
Here comes another deadly raid,
It certainly was far from grand.

Last night I heard the city triumph,
Peace restored at last,
A massive celebration began,
C'mon, let's have a glass!

Alex Kennedy Mann (8)
William Patten Primary School, Stoke Newington

Last Night In World War II

Last night I saw the city burning,
Bombs dropping, making houses burn,
People running and screaming
At the Germans invading us.

Last night I heard the city crashing,
Bombs diving like pelicans,
People yelping at each other,
Prayers coming from the city.

Last night I felt the city crying,
Bombs falling down like rain,
People crying and screaming,
While the Germans fight.

Last night I smelt the city celebrating,
People partying,
Colourful fireworks in the sky,
Dancing soldiers everywhere.

Natasha Montague (8)
William Patten Primary School, Stoke Newington

217

Last Night In World War II

Last night I smelt the city smoking,
As hot as the centre of the sun,
I hope this war will soon be over,
Then we will no longer have to run.

Last night I saw the city ablaze,
Bombs lit up the sky by
Fireworks' bright light,
Zooming across like a firefly.

Last night I heard the city screaming,
The noise filled my ears,
People panicking like nervous rabbits,
A lot of worries and fears.

Last night I heard the city celebrating,
Cheers let us satisfaction,
People laughed, glad that the war was over,
As they cleared up the destruction.

Orla Dolan (8)
William Patten Primary School, Stoke Newington

Scribbler! Magazine

If you enjoy reading and writing you will love Scribbler! Magazine.
Scribbler! Magazine will teach you new skills and build confidence
in your writing, whilst giving you lots of fun and entertainment.

We receive 100% positive feedback and are proud to say that
Scribbler! is the leading reading and writing magazine for 7-11
year olds. Jam packed with workshops, competitions, reviews and
lots more, Scribbler! will keep you entertained for hours.
To find out more about Scribbler! Magazine please visit our
website **www.scribblermagazine.com**

Young Writers Information

We hope you have enjoyed reading
this book - and that you will continue
to enjoy it in the coming years.

If you like reading and writing
poetry drop us a line, or give
us a call, and we'll send you
a free information pack.

Alternatively if you would like to order further
copies of this book or any of our other titles,
then please give us a call or log onto our
website at www.youngwriters.co.uk

Young Writers Information
Remus House
Coltsfoot Drive
Peterborough
PE2 9BF
(01733) 890066